THIS BOOK IS DEDICATED
to the memory of
VESTA HOLT
who started me,

and to
G.W. PRESCOTT
who showed me the way

PREFACE

The present book had its origins in two illustrated keys to genera of inland waters (1974) and of marine planktonic diatoms (1975), both of which were out of print in early 1979. The interest thus shown in diatom taxonomy suggested that a new book should be attempted to include not only an illustrated key combining the freshwater (with brackish) and marine, but also to provide a complete description of each genus to better verify the determination at this taxonomic level. This latter feature should benefit the user considerably since the references otherwise required may not be readily available and are quite expensive. Generic names of diatoms are mostly descriptive and their derivations may be of value to the user in learning and in association of the name with the organism. A complete listing of the genera with Greek (mostly) and Latin derivations has thus been included.

Taxonomy aside, the remainder of the book deals with general features of the biology of diatoms, presented so that they might be better appreciated as living, functioning, and interacting organisms in the ecosystem. The attempt here has been to introduce and to stimulate the interest in the biological aspects and not to produce a definitive or comprehensive survey of them. Other authors (notably Werner 1977, *Biology of Diatoms*) have provided the details; these can be found in the list of references and their bibliographies. It will be seen that the material in each section overlaps in greater or lesser degree with that of others, and this suggests the utility of the term "biology" as compared (arbitrarily) with "taxonomy" in its traditional usage.

Of the 110 genera in the present book, 14 were not included in the original *Keys*. These added genera are mostly from the eastern coastal region of North America. It is hoped, therefore, that these will add to the book's usefulness over a wider region. Most of the genera of diatoms are cosmopolitan in distribution, however, and many if not most could be encountered on either coast and far to the south. It may be of interest, for example, that a comparison with the list of genera reported by Prescott (1979 . A Contribution to the Bibliography of Antarctic and Subantarctic Algae. Bibliotheca Phycologia vol. 45. 312 pp.) indicates that 55 of the 70 genera reported from that region are treated in the present book.

It should be noted that the text, references, and genera included emphasize the plankton over the benthic forms (particularly the marine genera). No attempt has been made for a balance. Much of the literature is weighted that way, primarily because of the far greater importance (or ease in collection?) of the plankton. Perhaps the usefulness of this book will be for the same reason.

ACKNOWLEDGEMENTS

Acknowledgements are made to Dr. John Tibbs, director of the University of Montana Biological Station for space and facilities used and to Dr. G. W. Prescott for the use of his library there. The assistance of David Rockwell Crabtree in assembling, and Tom Pratte for inking many of the figures, is very much appreciated. The sources of the illustrations are given with the figure legend by number corresponding to the listing in the Taxonomic References. A large number of the figures of marine diatoms are from Cupp (1943) with permission of the University of California Press.

CONTENTS

Biology of Diatoms

Collection Techniques

Taxonomy of Diatoms

Derivations of Generic Names

Glossary of Taxonomic Terms

Explanation of Figures

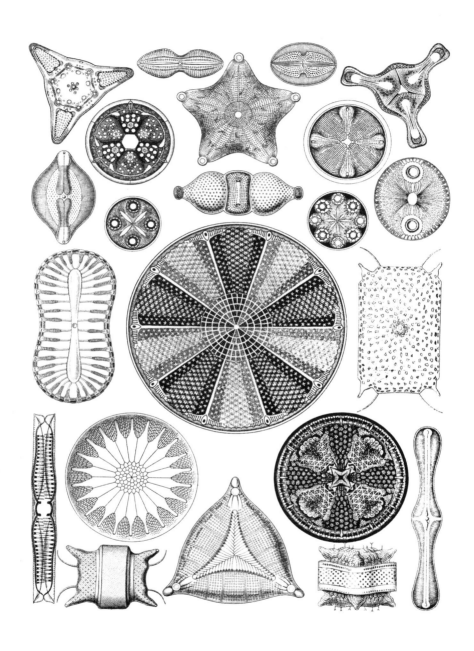

Marine Diatoms
By Ernst Haeckel, 1904. (Courtesy of Dover Publications, *Artforms in Nature*, 1974.)

BIOLOGY OF DIATOMS

General Characteristics

Diatoms include a large number of genera of microscopic algae inhabiting a great variety of aquatic habitats, such as brackish or marine waters. Perhaps the habitats excluded are hot springs in which certain bluegreen algae flourish or waters in which toxic minerals occur.

Though mostly microscopic, attached diatom growths may often be recognized as such by their brown color and feathery or furry appearance on such substrates as aquatic vascular plants or on seaweeds. Free-floating forms, however, may not be readily recognized as such since other types of algae may appear similar.

Microscopically diatoms are readily recognized by their distinctive shapes of two general types: elongate, cigar-shaped (or pen-like, thus **pennate**); or they may be disk-, drum-shaped or cylindrical (**centric**). (Unfortunately for the beginner, intermediate forms may also be encountered.) The cell wall of the elongate pennate types are typically ornamented with delicate lines in bilateral symmetry, with reference to the long axis. The drum-shaped centric group are characterized by radical symmetry, the lines arranged about a central point from which they radiate like spokes of a wheel.

Whatever the shape, diatoms all share a unique structural feature which is not so readily observable under the microscope. The cell walls are siliceous and of two separating (Greek di, two,+ tom, to cut) halves, one, the **epivalve**, overlapping the other, the **hypovalve**, like a petri dish. Because of the resistant nature of the silicon in the wall, dead cells of diatoms survive long periods of time as fossils. Incidentally, a general term for these organisms in German is "Kieselalgen"--translated, "glass-algae." Thus they live in glass houses.

Since one valve overlaps the other, they are of two sizes. The two may otherwise be identical in markings or ornamentation, but in some genera they differ, to greater or lesser degree.

With cell walls of this kind, as the two valves separate following cell division, new valves are produced within the two valves of the parent cell. Thus, as division continues, cell size must continuously be reduced--in one line. The epivalve, however, continues to produce hypovalves of similar size--generation after cell generation. At some minimal size, the cell contents forms a rejuvenescent cell, or **auxospore**, which on germination produces the full size valves characteristic of a given genus.

Yet another feature characterizes (some, not all) diatoms. This is the capability of spontaneous movement, of a very distinctive sort which is related to wall structure, and which has not counterpart elsewhere in the biological world. Those cells capable of movement in all cases are pennate forms having a slit-like groove, the **raphe**, in one or both valve surfaces. Not all pennate diatoms have this feature. When such surfaces with raphes are in contact with a substrate, they glide back and forth.

1

Diatomologists may not yet be in total agreement as to what actually propels these cells, but the structure of the raphe is suggestive. Raphes are characterized by being interrupted in the central part of the cell, and thus are two-parted. At opposite ends of cells are pore-like terminal nodules, and near each side of the central area are central nodules. One proposal from long ago suggested that cytoplasm streams from an apical nodule along the raphe to the central nodule, in a similar direction on each whole valve surface, but in the opposite direction on the other surface. Thus a sort of "caterpillar-tractor-tread" movement was envisioned.

More recent observations have demonstrated that "slime trails" are left behind as such diatoms move, such sticky trails even causing sand grains to adhere. This secretion apparently accounts also for the adhesion of the cells to a substrate. (Werner 1977)

Whatever the propulsion mechanism, a considerable variation in rates of movement has been noted among different free-living test cells, ranging from 0.2 to 25 μm/sec; tube-dwelling species have been clocked at up to 500 μm/sec. (Werner 1977)

A bizarre case of movement is illustrated by the highly animated filamentous species, *Nitzschia paradoxa* (Fig. 141), of fresh, brackish and marine coastal waters. In this diatom flat filaments are formed, with each cell moving relative to the adjacent one so that irregular filament margins may result. Each cell progressing in opposite direction from the adjacent, results in a linear extension (like an unfolded carpenter's rule); reversal brings the cells back into the original broad ribbon shape (rule folded). Van Heurck (1896) described the action as ". . . shooting into long filaments, then suddenly retreating until the filament is closed again, one frustule (cell) sliding past the other in a most marvelous manner." Under the microscope they may thrash about considerably.

The contents of a living cell include, in addition to nucleus and cytoplasm, chromoplasts (color bodies) of a yellowish to brownish or brownish-green pigments which include chlorophyll-a (in all green plants) and chlorophyll-c (shared also by brown seaweeds and some other algae), along with beta-carotene (also in all green plants) and brownish pigments. These latter include fucoxanthin, diadinoxanthin and diatoxanthin as accessory pigments. Chromoplasts of diatoms vary in size and shape, ranging from granules to disks or plates.

Included conspicuously in many living cells are more or less spherical, bluish-refringent oil droplets, a food reserve. The presence of these is dependant on the physiological state of the cell.

Many diatoms are solitary, but others having divided, remain in groups to form colonies held together only by secreted gelatinous material in amorphous clusters, or in gelatinous tubes. Some may adhere directly to a substrate. Others may secrete a stalk which attaches them to a substrate. With continued division, the stalks may become much branched. Still others secrete gelatinous pads at cell angles which result in a zigzag arrangement of cells. Many produce a linear arrangement of cells (filaments) which are connected by gelatinous threads; others by interlocking of spines produced by the cells (chains), or others by direct

2

fusion of cell wall surfaces. A given genus may be characterized by but one of these multicellular types, whereas others may be of more than one form.

Filaments may be more or less cylindrical (centric) or may be flat ribbons. A rather bizarre type of connection is illustrated by the centric fossil species (from Barbados), *Syndetocystis barbadensis*, which has hooks at each end of the cell which interlock with those of adjacent cells to form distinctive chains (see cover).

The numbers of species of diatoms have been estimated by various authors, with figures ranging from 12,000 to 100,000 described, with one proposal that 10,000 species only are valid (Guillard and Kilham 1977). This at any rate suggests a considerable range in variation among genera. Considering their variability, the range in cell sizes among the general treated herein, is about 1.5 x 3.0 μm in *Chaetoceros galvestonensis* (Fig. 68) to 1-4 mm long by 3-6 μm wide in *Thalassiothrix longissima* (Fig. 101).

Fossil Diatoms

From the fossil evidence it would appear that diatoms are relative newcomers on the scene, as compared to some other algal groups. Though there have been reports from the Paleozoic Era (time), they have not been absolutely verified as being diatoms. At least they are known from the Jurassic Period (see Partial Geologic Timetable) and occur in varying abundance throughout the Mesozoic and Cenozoic Eras. Their apparent absence in earlier strata does not, however, prove them to be only of more recent age since silicon does dissolve away under certain chemical conditions. (Delevoryas 1962)

Not all diatoms are silicified or are only weakly so (and these are rare) and thus may have been present but did not become fossilized. Furthermore it has been demonstrated in laboratory experiments that under different chemical treatments, such as might occur naturally, otherwise resistant forms do dissolve away--and at different rates depending on the species. Therefore an analysis of the species composition of a given fossil deposit may not reveal all of the original forms. (Werner 1977)

Marine species are known unmistakenly from the Jurassic Period, but fossil freshwater forms date back to the Oligocene Epoch, but most extensively to the Miocene (Delevoryas). The evidence thus suggests a marine origin for the group. It is of some evolutionary interest that centric forms predominate in the more ancient strata--and predominate in the oceans of today. A given species may be fossil as well as recent, though many fossil forms are apparently now extinct.

With the continuous rain to the bottom of lakes, estuaries and oceans, over long periods of gelogical time, the frustules of diatoms have accumulated in vast deposits known by the terms diatomite, diatomaceous earth, or Kieselguhr (German), and a number of industry trade names which give no hint of the contents. Vast areas of ocean floor are now covered with diatomaceous "ooze," as are the bottoms of inland lakes. Where exposed subsequently by geological processes these may have attained depths of a few, to some hundreds of feet and may be mined for their various uses. Such deposits represent former aquatic inland or coastal habitats where conditions were exceptionally favorable for growth by cell division, undisturbed for long periods.

The United States is the greatest producer of diatomite and California has the largest resources. The largest exposed deposit in the state occurs at Lompoc near Santa Barbara on the southern coast. This extends for miles and is at least 1,000 feet in depth. Nearby in the Santa Maria Oil fields is a subterranean deposit which is reported to be about 3,000 feet thick. The Lompoc area has the most extensive known deposits of high quality marine origin in the world. These are of Miocene-Pleiocene age.

Commercial deposits of freshwater diatomite are of widespread occurence in many of the states and with depths ranging generally up to 30 or 40 feet. In northeastern California near the town of Burney and Lake Britton (impoundment of Pit River) is an exposed deposit of several hundred feet in thickness and extending for at least 10 miles along the Pit River Canyon. An especially striking display is handily (for the roadside geologist) exposed in a road cut at Hat Creek where it joins the Pit. Here a layer of abot 30 feet in thickness, stark white, is capped by a black layer of basalt. Volcanic activity during the Miocene Epoch resulted in impoundments by lava dams. More recent lava flows in this area (just north of volcanic Mt. Lassen) have covered these deposits so their actual total extent is unknown. It is not unusual for diatomite to occur in volcanic areas, especially in the western states; and this suggests that volcanic ash, rich in silicon, provided this essential nutrient for especially lush growths of diatoms.

It should be noted in passing that sampling of river plankton should take into consideration the possibility of "contamination" with fossil forms, should the stream cut through diatomaceous deposits.

Because of distinctive differences between most marine and freshwater forms, an analysis of the diatoms in a given deposit is useful for studies of geochronology, or as indicators of paleoecological conditions. The former presence of a given type of habitat may thus be indicated by the fossil diatoms.

The unique characteristics which make diatomite of increasing commercial value result notably from the resistant silicon content of the frustule, and from the pore space involved. Though appearing under the microscope as more or less solid sheet glass, the walls actually are abundantly perforated--sieve-like. This feature is revealed especially well by the electron microscope. The pore-space accounts for a very considerable proportion of diatomite volume and because of this the density is much less than water, on which it will float--until becoming waterlogged. Though varying from one deposit to another, the product weight is only about one-seventh that of water. It may be capable of absorbing as much as eight times the amount of actual solid diatomite substance in a given volume. (Conger 1936)

A few hundred uses have been indicated for diatomite, and others will

4

surely be added. Ten main categories are listed by Clark (1978) as follows: filters (most important), mineral fillers, insulating material, fine abrasives (silver polishes, etc.), absorbents (related to pore space), catalysts, reactive silica source, structural materials (mainly lightweight aggregate), pozzolans (cement admixture), and conditioners or anticaking agents.

Whatever the product the diatomite is best fitted for must be determined microscopically. The most abundant species, or mix of species along with sizes and shapes predetermines the best use for the final product. A fine abrasive for silver polish requires a different grade from its uses as a filler in paints or for insulated bricks. Impurities too, must be noted under the microscope for purposes of grading.

Finally it should be noted that many of the uses of diatomite simply are not matched by any other material, and it is quite inconceivable ("in the forseeable future") that there will be developed synthetic substitutes; particularly since there are such vast untapped deposits available. The uniqueness of the product is determined by the uniqueness of the individual microscopic cells composing it. A tribute to these who live in glass houses.

Partial Geologic Timetable

(from Delevoryas 1962)

ERA	PERIOD	EPOCH	Beginning of Interval (Million Years)
		Pleistocene	1
CENOZOIC	TERTIARY	Pliocene	13
		Miocene	25
		Oligocene	36
		Eocene	58
		Paleocene	63
MESOZOIC	CRETACEOUS		135
	JURASSIC		181
	TRIASSIC		230

Ecology and Distribution

Diatoms long have been known as "primary producers," the "pasturage of the sea," etc. Their relative contribution as food and oxygen producers have been speculated upon for some time. In the early 1950's Rabinowitch (1955), a prominent biochemist, estimated the contribution of marine microscopic algae generally, to be some 90% of the world total. The diatoms, being better known than the dinoflagellates, with whom they share the ocean, were subsequently presumed to be the algae involved. A noted radio entertainer, with an environmental interest, extolled the virtues of diatoms as producing the 90%. And so they received even more publicity. More recently, with more than just speculation as a basis, the figure has been reduced to 40%, and the diatom fraction to be 20 to 25% of the world net primary production. (Werner, 1977)

In the oceans numbers or biomass figures are far greater in coastal areas where nutrients are in greatest abundance, being provided by runoff from the land, and by upwelling of nutrient-rich waters from the depths. Off-shore their numbers are much reduced. In calculations of abundance only plankton have been considered, whereas vast numbers of attached or benthic forms have not--simply because of the troublesome problems in their sampling.

The distribution of diatoms is important in ecology since individual species are adapted to varied habitats. In a general way they may be classified as to whether freshwater, brackish or marine; whether planktonic or benthic and/or oceanic (off-shore); and whether tropical, temperate or polar. Genera or species may overlap the boundaries of any of these sets of classes but many of the diatoms are limited to one or the other of them by reason of their specific adaptations.

Inland fresh and brackish habitats are far more varied. Brackish habitats inland may have similarities to marine brackish or may not. The nature and ratio of the specific salts in solution are important. Freshwater habitats with distinctive species are as follows (Patrick 1977): aerial, wet; aerial, very wet (eg., *Sphagnum* tips); wet caves with light; spray zones of lakes and rivers; wet margins of lakes and rivers; dry rocks; dry moss; and soils. A comparable listing for marine littoral habitats by McIntire and Moor (1977): upper intertidal; below mean high water; brackish tidepools; marine littoral; reefs and boulders; lower littoral; epiphytic, attached by mucilage pads or stalks, by tubes, or in gelatinous matrix; and sand.

Though diatoms are well known as occuring in great numbers in polar seas, it is not so commonly realized that a number of them flourish on ice floes to the extent of coloring them a yellowish or dingy brown. Apparently neither the substrate not the temperature is as important as the increased nutrient concentration on the surface of the ice. As freezing of the water occurs minerals in solution are "squeezed" out-- the original "applejack" technique for concentrating and separating solutes from the water. In coastal areas of both polar regions, the grinding action of glaciers produces an abundance of mineral nutrients which become available to the algae generally.

Diatoms of inland habitats apparently are not characteristic of ice surfaces in a similar way, but are occasionally encountered in snow or ice samples. In most cases such reports do not indicate whether the diatoms were living, or just incidental air-borne empty frustules. One occurrence of living diatom cells in submersed ice-cups in an epiglacial pond has been reported from Jasper National Park (Wharton and Vinyard 1978).

Another unusual habitat for inland forms is in oil field sump ponds in which they have been observed by the author (unpublished) in abundance--in certain Oklahoma ponds. In one such sample cells were contained within suspended oil droplets, lined up in rows--and in decreasing sizes.

In whatever the habitat, their ecological role which they share with other algae and higher plants, is that of producers of energy (food), and of oxygen. The term "primary producers," incidentally, gives no hint of the oxygen, produced in nature only by the process of photosynthesis, and without which the foods could not be utilized.

The requirements for photosynthesis and growth are in general those of other plants but with certain exceptions. Thus they require light of the right intensity, carbon dioxide and minerals in the right concentrations (notably silicon of course). Certain of the diatoms require in addition to these standard "plant nutrients," vitamin B12 and/or thiamin, and perhaps biotin. This additional requirement, shared with certain other algae (notable flagellates) is referred to by the term **auxotrophic**.

Any given species is genetically adapted to certain ranges of intensity (ranges of tolerance) for all of the environmental factors. These requirements being met, the species thrives and reproduces--providing they got to the "right" habitat to which they are preadapted. As to the matter of how a diatom gets from here to there, in many cases the explanation appears to be by wind currents. Bubbles bursting from the surface of the ocean, or even of sewage lagoons, have been observed to contain particulate matter. A given diatom cell may thus become the nucleus of a fog- or raindrop. Furthermore sea foam (often containing large numbers of diatoms) has been observed on glaciers in New Zealand; perhaps a form of mass transit. Presumably similar processes are effective in inland waters.

Sessile diatoms may attach to animals or to ships and be transported to far away places where they become dislodged. Old "balast dumps" in harbors thus may provide good collections of exotic forms. Incidentally, the "Sulfur-Bottom" whale is the Blue Whale with conspicuous growths of attached diatoms.

If migration is to be effective, of course, the living diatom cell must have arrived in viable conditions, and thus must have been capable of withstanding dessication. Living cells of diatoms (along with other algae) have been collected from the atmosphere and their viability established subsequently in cultures. Length of dormancy could not be determined. Hoover (1979), however, states that after adding water to a diatom dried on paper in 1834, he observed movement--nearly 150 years later.

A useful system of classifying **inland planktonic** habitats is one based on trophic, or relative "feeding"-capability of a given body of water. Feeding here implies mineral nutrient availability. Thus the term **oligotrophic** (poor + feeder) implies poor in mineral nutrients and thus poor in numbers of plants (and of animals feeding upon them). **Eutrophic** (true + feeder) indicates a habitat rich in mineral nutrients and rich in plant growth. Oligotrophic lakes thus are those with clear waters, whereas eutrophic are subject to dense algal blooms.

For practical purposes, oligotrophic implies unpolluted, and eutrophic polluted. Eutrophic lakes may be naturally so or artificially produced by pollution (cultural eutrophy). Two sriking examples of natural eutrophic conditions are Clear Lake in northwestern California, and Upper Klamath Lake in extreme south-central Oregon. These quite similar lakes became eutrophic long before settlers arrived, as a consequence of nitrogen fixation by blue-green algae. Phosphorus and other nutrients are readily available in both areas of volcanic activity, probably by "fertilization" with volcanic ash from nearby volcanos.

Eutrophication is the term which implies the process of enrichment, by whatever means, in a continuous series of stages. A recent addition to stage names is **pleioeutrophic** (late + feeder) which refers to sewage lagoons (perhaps coined as a euphonysm).

Some diatoms appear to be characteristic of oligotrophic lakes, and others of eutrophic. They are then referred to as "indicator" species, if their presence is restricted to one or another of the stages. As a group, the centric diatoms pre-dominate over the pennate in eutrophic waters, at least in some areas.

Plankters, being drifters, in order to continue to function as photosynthesizers, must somehow stay afloat in the upper region of a body of water where light penetrates in adequate amounts (the euphotic zone) for the process. One adaptation for bouyancy is the presence of long spines which increases the surface area of the cell. A great number of genera lack such structures, however. Another adaptation is the taking up of ions of lesser specific gravity than the water. The accumulation of oils and perhaps of metabolic gases also may aid in flotation.

Currents of one origin or another may be effective in maintaining the plankters in the upper water levels. Notable is the action of Langmuir circulation. Surface winds bring about circular, spiraling, elongate cells of water near the surface. Moving downwind, downwelling is followed by reversing, followed by upwelling. As observed from above, parallel windows mark the lines of downwelling. In those parts of the "cell" where the rate of movement is greatest plankters may descent to the depths, whereas large numbers remain in suspension. (Fogg, 1975)

Though it is important to stay afloat, there is an advantage to a cell in sinking. Since nutrients are taken up by diffusion through the cell wall there will be depletion in the immediate vicinity. Sinking brings the diatoms into regions of greater concentration of minerals and dissolved gases. The advantage of Langmuir currents is that the nutrients are mixed with the plankters. Those diatoms which attach to whales or ships have their nutrition problems solved in quite a different way.

In benthic habitats certain raphe-bearing forms are capable of migrating within mud or sand, reaching the surface layers where nutrients and light are more favorable. Those living within tubes may likewise move back and forth. Periods of increased motility are around sunrise for upward movement and around sunset for moving downward. Migration appears to be governed by the interaction of rhythms of motility, phototaxis, geotaxis and disturbance. (Harper, 1977)

Under favorable conditions for growth a diatom population may be stimulated to the extent that they may color the water or be observable otherwise. Such a growth is referred to as a "bloom." Commonly an increase in nitrates and, more importantly phosphates initiate the growth. This presumes that these two nutrients were in relatively short supply (thus "limiting") and other minerals adequate along with light and carbon dioxide. Continuous blooms may occur in shallow, nutrient-rich tropical ponds. Total numbers of cells involved may differ widely as may the size of the species involved. For example, Conger (1941) reports 5 million cells per liter for Synedra delicatissima, small freshwater diatoms in the Potomac River, whereas Cupp (1943) cites 2 million per liter for the marine Skeletonema costatum off southern California.

The duration of a phytoplankton bloom varies with the conditions for growth. As nutrients are depleted during a bloom, and as light penetration is reduced by the accumulated cells, reproduction may cease. If not consumed by animals the population dies and decomposes—mostly on the lake or ocean floor. With a continuing supply of nutrients, however, the bloom may persist. The diatom bloom in the Potomac River reported by Conger (l.c.) lasted for 20 days. Analyses of date by Tont (1976) from 20 years of daily sampling from the end of the pier at Scripps Institution of Oceanography (the longest daily sampling period ever) showed three blooms per year. Varying numbers and species were noted with the average duration of 5.5 weeks. Origin of the nutrients involved in that region are from various directions, as well as from upwelling.

In deep inland lakes in north temperate regions, during winter when conditions for growth are unfavorable, nutrients accumulate on the bottom in the form of dead cells or bodies of organisms. Almost no mixing of water takes place (particularly if frozen over) and a period of stagnation results. During the Spring, with increasing air temperature, any ice melts and the winds begin to mix the water. Since it is of more or less uniform temperature, and thus density, the whole of the water mass is affected and the result is an "overturn" of nutrient-rich waters from the depths, and uniform mixing results. At this time a spring diatom "pulse" or bloom occurs. A decline in the population follows and other algae may predominate.

During the summer another period of stagnation comes about as the upper layers are warmed. These are of lesser density than the colder lower water below, which may approach 4°C. A unique characteristic of water is the extreme resistance to mixing of layers differing in density—and density increases with decreasing temperature to about 4°C, then decreases until ice is formed. The upper layer (**epilimnion**) is isolated from the lower (**hypolimnion**) by a layer of temperature change (**thermocline or metalimnion**). This condition is referred to as thermal stratification. The epilimnion, more or less equivalent to the euphotic zone (depth to which effective light for photosynthesis penetrates), continues to be mixed by the winds. As summer progresses, the epilimnion is generally depleted of nutrients by the phytoplankton as dead organic matter continues to accumulate in the hypolimnion. Again in the fall, as heat is lost from the epilimnion to the cooler atmosphere, a uniform temperature occurs throughout the water mass. Fall winds bring about mixing of the water, now of uniform density, and a fall overturn again recycles the minerals from the depths. This often results in a fall pulse of diatoms, or in some lakes, other algae may be involved. This process is especially important for the recycling of phosphorus.

In the marine environment the nutrient supply also depends on cycling and transport by currents, but the mechanics differ. Oceans are more or less permanently stratified (especially those of great depth) so there is no overturn. Sub-surface as well as surface currents may, however, renew the nutrients stimulating diatom growth. Upwelling is especially effective in nutrient cycling. As prevailing winds move the surface waters offshore, they are replaced by nutrient-rich lower, colder waters which are brought up along the shore. Such areas of upwelling, as off the coast of California, are notably high in production of phytoplankton.

A variety of physical factors are involved in influencing the vertical temperature gradients (change of temperature with depth), including energy transfer at the sea surface and water movement below, the proximity to shore, and the latitude. Examples of these are illustrated in La Fond (1954).

The importance of diatoms to other organisms as a direct food source, or their position at the base of the food chain, is indicated by the term primary producers. As a good source otherwise, they may become the victims of parasites (notably fungi). Little is known, however, about the relative importance of the diatoms in this relationship, especially in marine waters. Certain other algae, notably bluegreens, may live symbiotically within diatom cells. Thus a number of diatom species (*Rhizosolenium, Chaetoceros, Bacteriastrum* and *Hemialus)* contain the blue-green algae *Richelia intracellularis*. This symbiont contains specialized cells called **heterocysts** which are associated with nitrogen fixation in blue-green algae generally. The infected cells are benefitted nutritionally even to the extent of bloom formation (Guillard and Kilhan 1977). A symbiotic occurence of a diatom within an animal cell is noted in the case of *Licmophora* whose naked cells may be found in the marine flatworm *Convoluta convoluta* (Bold and Wynne 1978). Otherwise, diatoms are not known to be parasitic, and none are known to be toxic to other organisms.

Changes in species composition and numbers are referred to as succession. These may result from a variety of factors operating together. Seasonal changes, resulting from variations in light concentration and temperature, are perhaps most commonly observed, as in terrestrial habitats. Changes in mineral nutrients or salinity may also be involved, perhaps resulting from runoff from the land, or from changes in oceanic currents. Less obvious changes may result from grazing, or interactions between the diatoms themselves. Diatom interactions are discussed under Physiology.

Structure and Reproduction

Cell walls of diatoms, as noted earlier, are composed of two halves, one covering the other as a lid of a petridish. The term **frustule** (Gr., a little bit or piece), though hardly descriptive, has long been used to refer (by some) to the whole cell including **epivalve** and **hypovalve** (or **epitheca** and **hypotheca**) and the protoplast contained, or to just the silicious shell with the protoplast removed. The wall is composed of two parts, an organic cell part of various constituents (said to be of a "pectic" nature), which surrounds the siliceous shell. The walls of zygotes or auxospores, however, are mainly organic but may include a silicious part.

The organic part of the wall stains specifically with ruthenium red while the cell is living, or recently alive. This fact becomes useful as medico-legal evidence for death by drowning in humans, when recently living diatoms are found within the alveolar spaces of their lungs, and thus distinguishable from air-borne dust of diatomite. (Duke and Reimann 1977).

The siliceous wall, highly porous, may have organic materials extruding from certain pores. These may appear as threads or bristles (Figs. 49-52) which are known to include glucoseamine in *Thalassiosira fluviatilis* (Fig. 48) and *Cyclotella cryptica*. Tubes such as are produced by *Amphipleura rutilans* contain other organic compounds, as do gelatinous stalks produced by many diatoms (Duke and Reiman, l.c.). Gelatinous pads, illustrated by *Isthmia nervosa* (Fig. 33), also are secreted from certain pores ("jelly pores") and account for their zigzag chain formation, or for their adherence to substrates.

The two valves are connected to each other by one or more mostly band-like, or scale-like in some (e.g. *Rhizosolenia*, Figs. 71, 74, 79) **girdle bands.**

Ornamentations are characteristic of the siliceous wall. A few diatoms lack silicon in the wall or are only weakly silicified, but delicate patterns in the organic layer may be ovserved with analin dyes. Three basic types of linear decorations include **punctae** (pores or depressions), **striae** (lines, which actually may be composed of delicate and closely spaced punctae), and **costae** (rib-like thickenings). Formed within the cell of some genera are thick partion-like, inward growths of the wall called **septa.** These may extend partly across the cell, or completely. They may extend partly across the cell, or completely. They may be flat as in *Diatomella* (Fig. 164) or undulate as in *Grammatophora* (Fig. 172), or

Illustrations of Diatom Cell Wall Structures

Structures and planes and axes of symmetry are illustrated in the following diagrams: A, pennate diatom with general features in oblique view; B, centric diatom in transverse section with structures indicated; C, centric diatom in oblique view with planes of symmetry; D, portion of pennate diatom in oblique view illustrating septa; E, pennate diatom in oblique view with planes of symmetry. *aa*, apical axis; *an*, apical nodule; *cn*, central nodule; *e*, epivalve; *g*, girdle; *gv*, girdle view; *h*, hypovalve; *m*, mantle (valve mantle); *pa*, pervalvar axis; *r*, raphe; *s*, septum; *ta*, transapical axis; *v*, valve; *vp*, valvar plane; *vv*, valve view. (From Fritsch, 1935).

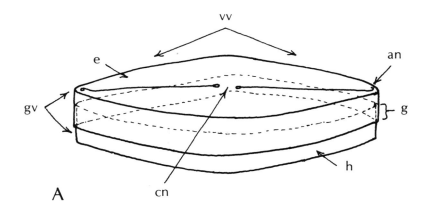

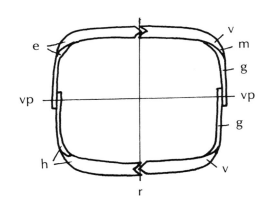

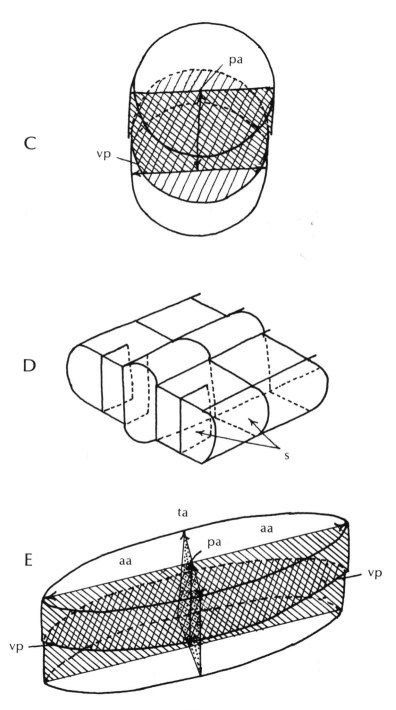

C

pa

vp

D

s

E

ta

aa

pa

aa

vp

vp

curved in the centric *Terpsinoe musica* (Fig. 29b). Septa will appear different in girdle as compared to valve views, and they may extend either longitudinally or transversely.

Present in many pennate (but not centric) genera is the raphe, a "V" -shaped slit-like structure on the valve surface and usually extending from each apex to near the center of the cell. Raphes are usually median in position in the long axis of the cell, but in some genera they are present on but one valve. In a few genera they lie near the margin or are excentric (Figs. 105, 113) and/or limited to a short length at either apex of the cell (Figs. 109, 119c). At either ends of the raphes are wall thickenings called nodules, a **central nodule** where they meet, and **polar nodules** at the extremities. Depending on the genus, raphes may be thin and thread-like, or broadened and **filamentous** (Figs. 154, 155) and either straight, "S-"shaped or **sigmoid** (Figs. 132-135; 143) or otherwise twisted (Fig. 139). In some genera the raphe lies between two siliceous ribs (Figs. 158-161) for a greater or lesser part of their length. In a few genera the raphe lies within a canal along the cell margin *(Nitzschia* and *Hantzschia),* or within **keels** which are wing-like structures. Within the canals or keels are a regular series of **keel punctae** or "carinal dots" (Latin. *carina,* keel) which are conspicuous along the margins of a cell (Figs. 140, 142, 143, 145, 147).

The **central area** of valves of pennate genera is hyaline or clear of striae (absent or shortened). In some cases isolated or groups of punctae may be present. A thickening of the central area across the valve is referred to as a **stauros** (Gr. *staur,* cross) as in *Stauroneis* (Fig. 151).

Areolae or **alveoli** are large pore-like structures within the walls of many centric genera. These are cavities or depressed chambers in the wall and perpendicular to it. They are honeycomb-like, and may be covered with a silica layer which is ornamented with fine punctae (Figs. 2, 18, 19, 32, 61, 85).

Reproduction in diatoms may be either vegetative (cell division) or sexual. It was noted earlier that cell division involves separation of epivalve and hypovalve, each having produced hypovalves. Successive divisions thus result in each valve becoming (or remaining) epivalves. In one line of progeny, a continued decrease in size results. At a certain minimal size sexual reproduction may be stimulated, and with the germination of zygotes or **auxospores,** cells of full "typical" size are produced. The cells of diatoms are diploid (diplont) and meiosis occurs with production of gametes. In centric diatoms certain cells become eggs and others produce two or more uniflagellate sperm, their numbers varying with the genus. Valves of egg cells separate and the egg is enlarged between them. Fusion of sperm and egg results in a zygote or auxospore of increased size usually with a highly ornamented wall.

In pennate diatoms, meiosis results in either one or two haploid gametes (depending on the genus), the other products of division ("polar nuclei") disintegrating. A gamete from one cell fuses with that of another to produce the zygote and auxospore. If two gametes are formed, these fuse; if one only is formed it fuses with that of another cell.

Variations in the details of sexual reproduction among diatoms are

14

given in Bold and Wynne (1978) and Drebes (1977).

Physiology

Physiology is the study of functioning of individuals, as compared to genetics, the functioning of populations. Physiological processes, furthermore, are regulated by stimulus-response reactions: no stimulus, no response.

Photosynthesis is the process in which solar energy is stored in the form of "foods" or photosynthetic reserves, water and carbon dioxide being the raw materials involved. From basic carbohydrates resulting from the process a variety of compounds may further by synthesized. Basic to the photosynthetic process in diatoms is the presence of the pigments Chlorophyll a and c, and the accessory pigments (which also absorb light) alpha and beta carotenes (orange), and several xanthophylls (yellow). These pigments are contained in plastids (chloroplasts, green; chromoplasts, colored) which number two to several per cell. The basic structure of the plastids is the thylakoid, or photosynthetic lamella, in diatoms arranged in groups of three. Food reserves include chrysolaminarin (leucosin) and lipid (oil) droplets.

The light quality effective in photosynthesis includes the red and blue-green wave lengths. Depths of penetration of these parts of the spectrum in a given body of water are thus limiting to the process.

Carbon dioxide required for the process is generally in adequate supply in a given habitat, being provided by respiration of all organisms including the diatoms themselves. The process of photosynthesis removes carbon dioxide from the water resulting in a decrease in acidity (higher pH) during daylight hours. During the night, increasing carbon dioxide concentrations increase the acidity (lower pH). The presence of buffers equalize these opposing changes in hydrogen ion concentration.

Mineral nutrients for diatoms are essentially those required by green plants generally, with the exception that silicon is a major nutrient, and sulphur is apparently involved in silicon utilization. Thus the major elements (macronutrients) required in high concentration are: carbon, hydrogen, oxygen, nitrogen, sulphur, phosphorus, potassium, magnesium, calcium (in algae), and silicon. The minor elements (micronutrients; trace elements) required in very small concentration are: sodium, iron, manganese, copper, zinc, molybdenum, vanadium, boron, chlorine, and cobalt. The "minor" elements, it should be noted, are of no minor importance but are just as essential as the major elements. These minor elements include the heavy metals which, except in trace amounts, may become toxic.

The availability òf any of the minerals to the plant may be dependant on interactions with other minerals, the pH of the medium (related to solubility) or due to the presence of chelators.

Chaelators (Gr. *chel*, claw; as the claw of a crab) are compounds which surround metalic ions (such as calcium, magnesium, iron, copper, manganese, mercury, etc.) tieing them up in a soluble form, isolating them in a "complex" where they can not react as metallic ions. The inclusion of chelators in detergents thus prevents the precipitation of calcium and magnesium in the wash. Synthetic detergents, often complex organic compounds such as ethylenediaminetetraacetic acid (EDTA), are used in household water softeners, or in laboratory cultures of algae (or other plants) to maintain minerals (especially iron) in a soluble form available to the algae. Naturally occuring chelators are notably present in brown bog waters.

Many algae, including a number of diatoms, require in addition to mineral nutrients, such complex organic compounds as the vitamins niacin (cobalamin; B12), thiamin (B1) and biotin either singly or in combination. Additionally, some may require amino acids. These are normally present in aquatic habitats, though in extremely low concentrations. They may become limiting under certain conditions. Laboratory cultures may require additions of these compounds in addition to the mineral nutrients.

The term auxotrophic (Gr. *aux*, a growth + *troph*, food) was coined to refer to the requirement of complex organic compounds; organotropohic is also used. Other related terms are autotrophic (photosynthetic; "self-feeder") and heterotrophic (utilizing organic matter; "different-feeder"). The diatoms mostly are autotrophic and many are auxotrophic, but few (eg. *Nitzschia putrida*) are heterotrophic. It is possible that many species are capable of heterotrophic nutrition for limited periods and under certain conditions (such as in Arctic blooms during very short days under ice).

Organic chemicals otherwise involved in algal physiology include "extracellular metabolites." These are secreted by living cells into the environment. Included are simple sugars and amino acids, but also certain compounds which inhibit the growth of other algae, or even of the species secreting them. Such growth inhibitors (antibiotics) thus may account for changes in species composition in a given habitat. Vitamins, including those involved in auxotrophy, also are secreted by some and these may be taken up and utilized by those species which do not synthesize them. This growth stimulation too may be of ecological importance. It is also possible that other chemicals secreted are repellant to animal feeders (this is apparently true of certain blue-green algae).

Economics

The importance of diatoms in a number of respects has been previously mentioned, but a few others remain.

In domestic water supplies the diatoms are beneficial in oxygenation and in nutrient uptake. In abundance they do on occasion affect the taste or odor of drinking water ("fishy or musty" odors), but are perhaps more important for their clogging of sand filters (Palmer 1959). At least, none are toxic.

Eutrophication in other waters may result in increased diatom production, though at higher nutrient levels they are replaced by other algae. Organic pollution appears to reduce the diversity, the complexity and the stability of a diatom community (Patrick 1964). The nature of the diatom community may itself thus become an indicator of pollution. As a group, the pennate species appear to be more sensitive than the centric, though one pennate species, *Nitzschia palea*, is typical of polluted waters and may be considered as an indicator of such conditions.

Pollutional conditions generally are inhibiting to diatom growth. As noted by Epply (1977) they appear to be relatively more sensitive than any other algal groups to many pollutants. He further states that, "It is interesting and significant that marine diatoms appear to be more sensitive to growth rate inhibition by chlorinated hydrocarbons (PCB's and DDT) than other unicellular algae tested."

In addition to these pollutants, an ever increasing pollutional threat in the oceans is from crude oil. Mostert (1974) cites a National Academy of Science report in 1973 stating that "1,370,000 tons of oil are being discharged into the sea every year during routine operations of tankers and other ships; in addition, accidents dumped another 350,000 tons." And the world's tanker fleet has grown considerably since then. Little, however, is known about the possible long term effects on the plankton. Epply (l.c.) cites one published paper (Pulich et al, 1974) and American Petroleum Institute (1979) summarizes the results of one study on phytoplankton. Neither of these refer to diatoms *per se*, however.

In recent years, with the growing concern over the increasing population and relative dwindling of food resources, the algae have been looked to as the ultimate way out. Laboratory test tube-to-pilot plant studies have proven that many algae, including diatoms, can be grown in mass cultures. Their nutritional characteristics establish them as adequate for at least a food supplement of a beneficial sort. A brighter day was seen ahead, awaiting only the technologists to sow and reap the harvest. Better yet, research at the University of California Sanitary Engineering Field Station at Richmond established that human wastes (sewage) could be converted into nutritionus algae (Oswald and Golueke 1968), and thus pollution problems could be resolved as well.

A futuristic point of view on the place of algae is illustrated in an address by then President of the University, Clark Kerr (having just visited the Richmond Lab) before the Ninth Biennial Wilderness Conference. He stated: ". . .These algae would supply all the food that man needed. So I saw the future of the world; it was the most efficient way for man to live. The whole world was covered with algae tanks, with little colonies on top of them, the algae cooking in the sun in this self-restoring process. There wasn't any going back into history. As far as anybody knew there had been algae tanks; as far as anybody could see ahead, algae tanks and more algae tanks. In traveling around the world, nothing but algae tanks every place." (Kerr 1966).

Quite a different point of view is illustrated by the biologist Odum (1971) who, in a section titled "Algal Culture and Fallacious Dreams"

17

states: "A cruel illusion was proffered by laboratory scientists and writers who proposed that we feed the world on algae which they implied were productive on a different order of magnitude from agriculture." He goes on to explain the high costs involved of subsidies of fossil fuel, energy for fertilizing, stirring, containing and distributing, controlling growth, and concentrating for harvest--these added to the initial high overhead involved in the installation of facilities. The actual efficiency of an algal system for food production thus is much reduced when all subsidies are considered (compare Oswald and Golueke 1968).

A thoughtful reminder: "There is no such thing as a free lunch." The importance of the diatoms and the future of all life in the oceans--and ultimately perhaps on the land--should be the concern of everyone on this planet. With increasing oil and pesticide pollution, the fate of the diatoms may lie in the balance. The regions of greatest production of diatoms are those of greatest food resource potential for man, these include, especially, the Southern Ocean and the North Sea, regions which now are threatened by massive oil pollution (the latter). Coastal regions generally, where diatoms flourish, are increasingly threatened with pollutional insults from the land. The dilemma for the future thus involves energy: energy for growing more people vs. energy for running more machines. Uniquely it is presumed by many that the diatoms themselves may be the original source of petroleum as a fossil fuel (and thus of the petro-chemicals including pesticides derived from it) which threaten them now.

Biological References

American Petroleum Institute. 1979., Oil and the Sea. American Petroleum Institute, Washington D.C. 22 pp., illus.

American Public Health Association. 1971. Standard Methods for the Examination of Water and Wastewater. 13th ed. American Public Health Association, WAshington D.C.. 874 pp.

Anonymous. 1969. Eutropication: Causes, Consequences, Correctives. Proceedings of a Symposium. .National Academy of Sciences, Washington, D.C. 661 pp.

Blum, J.L. 1956. The Ecology of River Algae. Bot. Reveiw 22(5): 192-341.

Bold, H.C. and M.J. Wynne. 1978. Introduction to the Algae. Prentice-Hall, Inc., New Jersey. 706 pp.

Boney, A.D. 1966. A Biology of the Marine Algae. Hutchinson Educational, Ltd., London. 216 pp.

Boney, A.D. 1975. Phytoplankton. Edward Arnold, Ltd. 116 pp.

Borror, D.J. 1960. Dictionary of Word Roots and Combining Forms. National Press Books, Palo Alto. 134 pp. (Paper)

Burke, J.F. 1937a. Collecting Recent Diatoms. New York Microscopical Soc. Bull. 1 (3): 9-12.

Burke, J.F. 1937b. Preparing Recent Diatoms. Ibid. 1(4): 13-16.

Burke, J.F. 1937c. Mounting Recent Diatoms. Ibid. 1(5): 17-20.

Calvert, R. 1930. Diatomaceous Earth. The Chemical Catalog Co., Inc. 251 pp., illus.

Clark, W.B. 1978. Diatomite Industry in California. Calif. Geol. Jan. 1978. pp. 3-9.

Cole, G.A. 1979. Textbook of Limnology. C.V. Mosby. 444pp., 147 illus.

Conger, P.S. 1937. Significance of Shell Structure in Diatoms. Ann. Rept. Board of Regents Smiths. Instit., 1936. pp. 325-344 + 19 pl. U.S. Gov. Printing Office.

Conger, P.S. 1941. Aspects of the Hydrobiological Importance of Diatoms. In, University of Wisconsin, A Symposium on Hydrobiology. pp. 396-397. University of Wisconsin Press, Madison.

Conger, P.S. 1950. A New Method for the Preservation of Diatoms and Other Siliceous Structures. Trans. Amer. Microsc. Soc. 69 (1): 66-68.

Cummins, A.B. and H. Mulryan. 1937. Diatomite. In, Industrial Minerals and Rocks. American Inst. of Mining and Metallurgical Engineers. pp. 243-260.

Cupp, E. 1943. Marine Plankton Diatoms of the West Coast of North America. Bull. Scripps Inst. Oceanogr. 5: 1-238.

Darley, W.M. 1977. Biochemical Composition. In, D. Werner (ed.), The Biology of Diatoms. pp. 198-223. Univ. California Press, Berkeley and Los Angeles.

Dawson, E.Y. 1966. Marine Botany, an Introduction. Holt, Rinehart and Winston, New York. xii + 371 pp., illus.

Delevoryas, T. 1962. Morphology and Evolution of Fossil Plants. Holt, Rinehart & Winston, New York. 189 pp.; illus.

Drebes, G. 1977. Sexuality. In, D. Werner, (ed.), The Bilolgy ofDiatoms. pp. 250-283. University of California Press, Berkeley and Los Angeles.

Drum, R.W. and J.T. Hopkins. 1966. Diatom Locomotion: An Explanation. Protoplasma 62(1): 1-33.

Duke, E.L. and B.E.F. Reimann. 1977. The Ultrastructure of the Diatom Cell. In, D. Werner (ed.), The Biology of Diatoms. pp. 65-109. University of California, Berkeley and Los Angeles.

Eppley, R.W. 1977. The Growth and Culture of Diatoms. In, D. Werner (ed), The Biology of Diatoms. pp. 24-64. University of California Press, Berkeley and Los Angeles.

Evans, F. 1964. The Future of Phycology. In, D.F. Jackson (ed.), Algae and Man. pp. 426-434. Plenum Press, New York.

Eyster, C. 1964. Micronutrient Requirements for Green Plants, Especially Algae. In, D.F. Jackson (ed.), Algae and Man. pp. 86-119. Plenum Press, New York.

Fitzgerald, G.P. 1964. The Biotic Relationships Within Water Blooms. In, D.F. Jackson (ed.), Algae and Man. pp. 300-306. Plenum Press, New York.

Fogg, G.E. 1964. Environmental Conditions and the Pattern of Metabolism in Algae. In, D.F. Jackson (ed.), Algae and Man. pp. 77-85. Plenum Press, New York.

Fogg. 1975. Algae Cultures and Phytoplankton Ecology.2d ed. University of Wisconsin Press, Madison. 175 pp., illus.

Fritsch, F.E. 1935. The Structure and Reproduction of the Algae. Vol. I. Cambridge University Press, London. xvii + 791 pp.

Goldman, C.R. (ed.). 1965. Primary Production in Aquatic Environment. Mem. Ist. Ital. Idrobiol., Suppl. 18. 471 pp.

Gray, P. 1972. Student Dictionary of Biology. Van Nostrand Reinhold Co., New York. 194 pp.

Guillard, R.R.L. and P. Kilham, 1977. The Ecology of Marine Plankton Diatoms. In, D. Werner (ed), The Biology of Diatoms. pp. 372-469. University of California Press, Berkeley and Los Angeles.

Harper, M.A. 1977. Movements. In, D. Werner (ed.), The Biology of Diatoms. pp. 224-249. University of California Press, Berkeley and Los Angeles.

Heynes, H.B.N. 1963. The Biology of Polluted Waters. Liverpool University Press, England. 202 pp.

Hoover, R.B. 1979. Those Marvelous Myriad Diatoms. National Geographic 155(6): 870-878. Illus.

Hutchinson, G.E. 1967. A Treatise on Limnology. Vol. II. Introduction to Lake Biology and the Limnoplankton. John Wiley & Sons, Inc., New York. 1115 pp.

Hutchinson, G.E. 1969. Eutrophication, Past and Present. In, (Anon.) Eutrophication: Causes, Consequences, Corrections. pp. 17-26. National Academy of Sciences, Washington D.C.

Hutchinson, G.E. 1973. Eutrophication. American Scientist 61: 269-279.

Ichimura, S. 1968. Phytoplankton Photosynthesis. In, D.F. Jackson (ed.), Algae, Man and the Environment. pp. 103-120. Syracuse University Press, New York.

Jackson, D.F. (ed.). 1964. algae and Man. Plenum Press, New York. 434 pp.

Jackson, D.F. 1968. Algae, Man, and the Environment. Syracuse University Press, New York. 554 pp.

Jaeger, E.C. 1955. A Source-Book of Biological Names and Terms. 3rd. ed. Charles C. Thomas, Springfield, Illinois. 323 pp.

Jorgensen, E.G. 1977. Photosiynthesis. In, D. Werner (ed.), The Biology of Diatoms. pp. 150-168. University of California Press, Berkeley and Los Angeles.

Kerr, C. 1966. Introduction. In, B.M. Kilgore (ed.), Wilderness in a Changing World. pp. 141-144. Sierra Club. San Francisco.

Kilgore, B.M. (ed.). 1966. Wilderness in a Changing World. Sierra Club, San Francisco. 251 pp.

La Fond, E. 1954. Factors Affecting Vertical Temperature Gradients in the Upper Layers of the Sea. Sci. Monthly April 1954: 243-253.

Lewin, J.C. and R.R.L. 1963. Diatoms. Ann. Rev. Microbiol. 17: 373-414.

Lind, Owen T. 1979. Handbook of Common Methods in Limnology 2nd ed. C.V. Mosby Co., St. Louis. 212 pp., 40 illus.

Lund, J.W.G. 1965. The Ecology of the Freshwater Phytoplankton. Biol. Rev. 40: 231-293.

Lund, J.W.G. 1969. Phytoplankton. In, (Anon.) Eutrophication: Causes, Consequences, Correctives. pp. 306-330 National Academy of Sciences, Washington D.C.

McIntire C.D. and W.W. Moore, 1977. Marine Littoral Diatoms: Ecol gical Considerations. In, D. Werner (ed.), The Biology of Diatoms. pp. 333-371. University of California Press, Berkeley and Los Angeles.

Munk, W.H. and G.A. Riley. 1952. Absorption of Nutrients by Aquatic Plants. J. Marine Research 11(2): 215-240.

Odum, H.T. 1971. Environment, Power and Society. John Wiley and Sons, Inc. ix + 331 pp., illus.

Oswald, W.J. and C.G. Golueke. 1968. Harvesting and Processing of Waste-grown Microalgae. In, D.F. Jackson (ed.), Algae, Man and the Environment. pp. 371-389. Syracuse University Press, New York.

Palmer, C.M. 1959. algae in Water Supplies. An Illustrated Manual on the Identification, Significance, and Control of Algae in Water Supplies. Public Health Service Pub. No. 657. U.S. Government Printing Office, Washington, D.C. 88 pp., illus.: figs + 6 color plates.

Palmer, C.M. 1964. Algae in Water Supplies of the United States. In, D.F. Jackson (ed.), Algae and Man. pp.239-261. Plenum Press, New York.

Papenfuss, G.F. 1955. Classification of the Algae. In, A Century of Progress in the Natural Sciences 1853-1953. pp 115-224. California Academy of Sciences, San Francisco.

Patrick, R. 1948. Factors Affecting the Distribution of Diatoms. Bot. Rev. 14(8): 473-524.

Patrick, R. 1964. A Discussion of Natural and Abnormal Diatom Communities, In D.F. Jackson (ed.), Algae and Man. pp. 185-204. Plenum Press, New York.

Patrick, R. 1970. Benthic Stream Communities. Amer. Scientist 58: 546-549.

Patrick, R. 1977. Ecology of Freshwater Diatoms and Diatom Communities. In, D. Werner (ed.), The Biology of Diatoms. pp. 284-332. University of California Press, Berkeley and Los Angeles.

Patrick, R. and C.W. Reimer. 1966. The Diatoms of the United States. Vol. 1. Monogr. Acad. Nat. Sci., Philadelphia No. 13. 688 pp, 64 pls.

Prescott, G.W. 1956. A Guide to Literature on Ecology and Life Hisitoreis of the Algae. Bot. Rev. 22(3): 167-240.

Prescott, G.W. 1968. The Algae: A Review. Houghton Mifflin Co., Boston. 436 pp., illus.

Provasoli, L. 1969. Algal Nutrition and Eutrophication. In, (Anon.), Eutrophication: Causes, Consequences, and Correctives. pp.574-593. National Academy of Sciences, Washington, D.C.

Pulich, W. M. Jr., K. Winters and C. VanBaalen. 1974. The Effects of No. 2 Fuel Oil and two Crude Oils on the Growth and Photosynthesis of Microalgae. Mar. Biol. 28: 87-94.

Rabinowitch, E.I. 1955. Photosynthesis. In, G. Piel et al (eds.), The Physics and Chemistry of Life. pp. 27-47 Simon and Schuster, New York.

Round, F.E. 1968. Light and Temperature: Some Aspects of Their Influence on Algae. In, D.F. Jackson (ed.), Algae, Man and The Environment. pp. 73-102. Syracuse University Press, New York.

Ryther, J.H. 1959. Potential Productivity of the Sea. Science 130: 602-608.

Round, F.E. 1964. The Ecology of Benthic Algae. In, D.F. Jackson (ed.), Algae and Man. pp. 138-184. Plenum Press, New York.

Round, F.E. 1973. The Biology of the algae. St. Martins Press, New York. 278 pp., illus.

Ryther, J. H. and W.M. Dunstan. 1971. Nitrogen, Phosphorus and Eutrophication in the Coastal Marine Environment. Science 171;

Smith, G.M. 1950. Fresh-water Algae of the United States. 2nd. ed. McGraw-Hill, New York. 719 pp., 559 figs.

Stein, J.R. (ed.). 1973. Handbook of Phycological Methods. Culture Methods and Growth Measurements. 448 pp. Cambridge University Press, Cambridge, England.

Trainor, F. R. 1978. Introductory Phycology. John Wiley and Sons, New York. 525 pp., illus.

University of Wisconsin. 1941. A Symposium on Hydrobiology. University of Wisconsin Press, Madison.

Van Heurck, H. 1896. A treatise on the Diatomaceae. Transl. by W.E. Baxter. (Reprint 1962, Wheldon & WEsley, Ltd., London). xx + 559 pp., 35 pls., 291 text figs..

Verduin, J. 1964. Principles of Primary Productivity: Photosynthesis Under Completely Natural Conditions. In, D.F. Jackson (ed.), Algae and Man. pp. 221-238. Plenum Press, New York.

Voss, G.L., S.Y. Barlowe and V.R. Webster. 1972. Oceanography. Western Publishing Co., Inc. 160 pp.

Welch, P.S. 1948. Limnological Methods. The Blakiston Co., Philadelphia. 381 pp.

Werner, D. (ed.). 1977a. The Biology of Diatoms. University of California Press, Berkeley and Los Angeles. 498 pp.

Werner, D. 1977b. Introduction With a Note on Taxonomy. In, D. Werner (ed.), The Biology of Diatoms. p. 1-17. University of California Press, Berkeley and Los Angeles.

Werner D. 1977c. Silicate Metabolism. In, D. Werner (ed.), The Biology of Diatoms. pp. 110-149. University of California Press, Berkeley and Los Angeles.

Wharton, R.A. and W.C. Vinyard. 1978. Algae of Snow and Ice. American Alpine News 4/Issure 147: 18-19.

Zarnecki, S. 1968. Algae and Fish Relationships. In, D.F. Jackson (ed.), Algae Man and the Environment. pp. 459-477. Syracuse University Press, New York.

COLLECTION TECHNIQUES

Methods of collecting diatoms are quite simple if only qualitative (compared to quantitative) samples are of concern. Imagination is important. Three general collecting devices or techniques are useful: a plankton net, for collecting and concentrating; a scraping device for **sessile** (attached) forms; and a large pipet for **benthic** or **epipelic** forms.

Plankton nets for algae should be of relatively fine mesh to catch the smaller forms. Commonly a No. 20 (173 meshes/inch; 0.076 mm) or No. 25 (200 meshes/inch; 0.064 mm) are used. Small size tow nets are the most useful in a variety of habitats, and may even be lined to a fishing rod and cast out some distance from shore.

Sessile forms must be scraped from the substrate and a spoon-like device with one flat side, attached to a pole or rod, aid in extending the reach.

Benthic or epipelic collections are easily made (in shallow water) with a "macropipet," such as a roast baster. Care must be taken not to disturb the substrate and cloud the water. Scuba diving gear ideally should be used in deeper waters.

Many algae, including diatoms, form floating mats which may simply be scooped up in a jar or vial ("hand-grabs").

Squeezings of aquatic vegetation may produce interesting forms, especially in *Sphagnum* (acid) bogs.

Snow or ice samples may be collected in plastic bags and allowed to melt (black trash bags speed up the melting), then concentrated by net or by settling.

If the samples are to be kept alive, due consideration must be given to their aeration: do not fill the sample vial, and do not seal them--or at least loosen the caps when possible. Store in a cool place out of direct sunlight.

Preservation of samples in 3-5% formalin (c. 4 ml commercial formalin in c. 96 ml of water) is satisfactory for diatoms as well as most other algae. The cell walls, of course, need not be preserved, but a putrid mess results if not. Incidentally, Conger (1950) suggests a preservative for diatoms consisting of 1.5-3 parts of HC1 in a sample of 100 parts plus the acid. The organic matter in the sample and the shells are cleaned while in storage.

If diatoms are to be analyzed quantitatively, a number of methods are available and can not be dealt with here. See Welch (1948), Lind (1979), and A.P.H.A. (1971).

Living samples may be maintained in cultures for various uses, such as for isolating individual cells to produce unialgal cultures. A simple and usually quite effective method is the soil-water culture method developed by Pringsheim (Eyster 1968): To a glass vessel add 1 part garden soil and 9 parts water (or sea water, preferably aged a few months). For a more basic (higher pH) media add a pinch of calcium carbonate before the soil. For more acidic, add a bit of peat. Some algae benefit from a pea cotyledon. Plug with cotton and steam 1 hour on each of two successive days. Allow media to clear before innoculation. Other methods are given in Bold and Wynne (1978), Prescott (1968), Stein (1973), and Trainor (1978).

Cultures may be placed in a north window (or use fluorescent illumination at about 20°C). Avoid direct sunlight. A week or so may be required for growth to become obvious.

Diatoms may be cleaned to remove any organic cellular material which otherwise obscures the ornamentations important for identification. A simple technique is by burning on a hot plate at a very high temperature. A drop of the diatom material is spread out on a coverslip which is then placed on the hot plate until the color changes, usually to gray or brownish. It is then inverted on a drop of mounting medium (see below) on a slide. It is finally heated to evaporate the solvent and a permanent slide results.

An alternate method involves treatment with acids (Conger l.c.). Details can be found in Patrick and Reimer (1966), Burke (1937 b), Cupp (1943), and van Heurck (1896).

In preparing the sample, whether treated with heat or acids, any sand must be removed by washing and decanting. If the sample is brackish or marine, the salt must be removed by carefully rinsing and decanting, or the coverslip with burned material can be dipped in distilled water to remove the salt. The salt will crystalize otherwise.

It should be noted that some diatoms with weakly silicified walls may be destroyed either by burning or by acid cleaning. These can be rinsed to remove the salt (if marine) and mounted directly in Pleurax. Cleaned diatoms otherwise should be mounted in Hyrax (available only from Custom Research and Development Inc., 18500 Mt. Vernon Rd., Auburn, CA 95603), Carmount (available from R.P. Cargille Laboratories Inc., Cedar Grove, NJ 07009) or Styrax. These have optical indexes different from that of the diatom cell wall or of the coverslip and slide.

Of course a great many diatoms can be identified (at least to genus) in water mounts, but this depends on their size, distinctive shape, and nature of the characteristic wall ornamentations. Species determination often will require oil emersion and a permanent mount thus is advisble.

TAXONOMY OF DIATOMS

Introduction

The taxonomic system which relates diatoms and other members of the Plant Kingdom is a hierarchy of categories or **taxa** (sing., **taxon**) with subdivisions. Thus the Kingdom is subdivided into Divisions (Phyla in the Animal Kingdom) named with the characteristic suffix -*phyta;* Divisions include classes, named with the suffix -*phyceae;* classes are subdivided into Orders, with the suffix -*ales;* and these include Families, named with the suffix -*aceae.* Genera, which make up families, have Latinized endings (though diatom generic names are predominantly of Greek origin; see Derivations of Generic Names). The names of **Species** (sing., also **species**) are composed of a generic name with a specific epithet (a descriptive term, generally). Thus the term "binomial (=two names) system of nomenclature."

There are different points of view as to the naming of the higher taxa which include diatoms. Thus one proposal (used by Bold and Wynne, 1978) includes as part of the name of a Division -*phyco*- (Gr., *alga*), as for example Chlorophycophyta (green algae) and Chrysophycophyta.

The position of the diatoms in the hierarchy also differs with various authors. Patrick and Reimer (1966) consider the diatoms as a separate Division and use the name Bacillariophyta; Bourrely (1968) similarly, but with the name Diatomophyta. Otherwise they are considered as a class Bacillariophyceae (or Diatomophyceae) in the division Chrysophyta (or Chrysophycophyta).

At the level of Order, again there are differences as to whether there is but one (Bacillariales) or as many as ten orders; and each of these have one or more families.

The intent of any taxonomic system is to indicate phylogenetic relationships among variable organisms. Thus closely related species are grouped in a Genus; closely related genera into Families, etc. Relationships at each taxon level, but perhaps more importantly at the level of Species, should be based on **phenotype** (the sum of all observable characters), and which should include physiology, life cycle details, and ecological characteristics. Thus the importance of studying organisms in living cultures, or at least as living samples. But of course, identity may not be revealed except in cleaned cell wall preparations.

A number of diatoms (and it is really too early to state how many) are **polymorphic** (= many forms) as illustrated by different forms observed under different culture conditions. For example, the **anomalous** (Latin, *irregular*) diatom *Phaeodactylum tricornutum (P. cornutus,* in Patrick and Reimer, 1966) has features both diatom-like (weakly siliceous walls) and non-diatom-like (non-siliceous), and shapes either oval or elliptical. The combinations of characters vary with cultural conditions.

The history of diatom taxonomy (as outlined by Papenfuss, 1955) dates back to 1773 when O.F. Muller described a species of *Gomphonema* as

Vorticella pyraria (a protozoan name). He later named *Vibrio paxillifer*, the name being changed subsequently to *Bacillaria* and used by some authors to include all of the rod-shaped diatoms. The present name *Nitzschia paradoxa* (Gmelin) Grunow is synonymous with *Bacillaria paradoxa* Gmelin, and *Vibrio paxillifer* Müller. The same diatom by any name. Until 1832 the diatoms were regarded partly as animals (the motile forms) and partly as algae (non-motile). The entire group then were becoming accepted as algae.

Key to the Genera of Marine and Freshwater Diatoms of the United States

The Key deals with the level of Genus. To identify an unknown genus, start first with the lines 1a and 1b. Choose between these two which "fits" or corresponds to the specimen. Each of these numbered sets refer to another pair of characters (e.g., 2a, 2b) from which another choice is made. Ultimately a generic name will be reached. The description of that genus should then be compared with the illustration(s) to verify the identity of the specimen.

It should be noted that the illustrations of a given genus do not necessarily match the specimen since there may be more than one species in a given genus, each with their differences. Additional taxonomic references might be consulted for illustrations of other species not included here.

DIATOMS CENTRIC. Valves with a concentric or radiating sculpture around a point or points, central or lateral, never arranged in relation to a middle line. Without raphe or pseudoraphe. Outline circular, oval, or elliptical, sometimes polygonal, rarely crescent-shaped or spindle-shaped. Processes common. (Cupp 1943).

1. Plants multicellular, variously colonial in gelatinous secretions, in attached series as filaments (ribbons or chains) or in a zigzag arrangement.. 2.

1. Cells solitary (including individual cells of multicellular diatoms) .... 32.

   2. Cells colonial in amorphous gelatinous Masses .... (F, M) *Thalassiosira* (Figs. 48-50, 80)

   2. Cells in distinct series or zigzag chains, either in loose chains united by gelatinous threads, more or less loosely filamentous by interlocking of siliceous spines, or by fusion of adjacent valve surfaces .... 3.

3. Cells drum-shaped, separated but in chains united by gelatinous threads .... 4.

3. Cells in zigzag chains or in distinct linear arrangement (filamentous) .... 6.

   4. Cells united by a single thread from valve center .... (F, M) *Thalassiosira* (Fig. 48-50, 80)

   4. Cells united by many threads and/or otherwise gelatinous pads .... 5.

29

5.   Cells united by 4-9 gelatinous threads .... (M) **Coscinosira** (Fig. 52)

5.   Cells united by 15-20 threads (Observable only with difficulty within otherwise amorphous gelatinous pads between connecting adjacent cells)........................ (M) **Porosira** (Fig. 57)

      6.   (3.) Cells in zigzag chains.. 7.

      6.   Cells more or less loosely united by setae............................. 9.

7.   Cells triangular (or 4- or 5-angled) in valve view .... (M) **Triceratium** (Fig. 32).

7.   Cells in valve view cylindrical or oval.. 8.

      8.   Cells with short processes or lobes from opposite sides of each valve end ....(F, M̲) **Biddulphia** (Figs. 21-28).

      8.   Cells without processes, trapezoidal, very large; walls highly sculptured... (M) **Isthmia** (Fig. 33)

9.   (6.) Cells more or less loosely united by setae radiating outward from valve ends .... 10.

9.   Cells without long radiating setae.. 11.

      10. Setae mostly very long, unbranched, spreading only from opposite sides of cell................. (F, M̲) **Chaetoceros** (Figs. 62-66, 68)

      10. Setae many, whorled, forked (except terminal setae unbranched) .... (M) **Bacteriastrum** (Figs. 67, 69)

11. (9.) Cells united by hollow setae or spines................................. 12.

11. Cells in firm filaments, bands or ribbons, cells held together by fused valve surfaces, or by fusion of blunt to elongate central or marginal lobes; spines lacking .... 15.

      12. Spines single, cells with numerous intercalary bands ...... 13.

      12. Spines numerous, hollow in marginal series on valve, these fusing with those of adjacent cell; lacking intercalary bands .... 14.

13. Spines excentric from opposite sides of valve; gelatinous hairs lacking (walls weakly silicified, ornamentation obscure in water mounts; destroyed in acid prepartions) .... (F, M)
Rhizosolenia (Figs. 71-75, 79)

13. Spine central from a depression in valve, margin of valve surrounded by gelatinous threads forking on joining those of adjacent cell to produce a characteristic zigzag .... (M)
Schroederella (Fig. 53)

   14. (12.) Valves conspicuously areolate (honeycomb-like)..........
(M) *Stephanopyxis* (Figs. 60, 61)

   14. Valves lacking ornamentation .... (M) *Skeletonema* (Fig. 59)

15. (11.) Cells in more or less flat filaments, valves linear to elliptical .... 16.

15. Cells triangular, quadrangular or cylindrical................................. 19.

   16. Valve surface flat with square outline, these united; filament strongly twisted .... (M) *Streptotheca* (Fig. 47)

   16. Valves concave, margins united so a large oval aperture is present between cells .... 17.

17. Cells straight, H-shaped, but filaments more or less twisted .... (M) *Climacodium* (Fig. 84)

17. Cells bent, forming curved filaments .... 18.

   18. Cells fused by pointed cell processes; filaments often twisted; wall more or less distinctly sculptured .... (M)
Hemiaulus (Figs. 82, 83)

   18. Cells fused to each other by blunt processes; filaments spirally curved; wall distinctly sculptured, punctate; intercalary bands present; filaments spirally curved .... (M)
Eucampia (Fig. 81)

19. (15.) Cells tri- or quadrangular .... 20.

19. Cells more or less cylindrical, not angular; filaments straight or twisted .... 23.

   20. Valves of adjacent cells fused at margins and centrally, leaving elliptical openings between contact points; walls unornamented; cells tri- or quadrangular .... (M)
Bellarochea (Figs. 44, 45)

   20. Valves fused by more or less flat surfaces; walls distinctly ornamented .... 21.

21.   Angles of valves constricted, broadly rounded at apices ....
      (F, B, M) *Hydrosera* (Fig. 85)

21.   Valve angles not as above, not acutely angled; walls more or less areolate .... 22.

22.   Valves with short processes at angles, without a central spine .... (M) *Triceratium* (Fig. 32)

22.   Valves without processes at angles but with a central hollow spine .... (M) *Lithodesmium* (Fig. 46)

23.   Cells with blunt cylindrical, conical or globular processes .... 24.

23.   Cells without conspicuous processes, but with minute spinules or small teeth on valves of some .... 25.

24.   Processes 2, blunt, near margin of valve, these attaching to those of adjacent cell by means of a fine, small curved hair-like process which fits into valve of adjacent cell; cells cylindrical, intercalary bands numerous; walls with delicate sculpture (walls weakly silicified) .... (M) *Ceratulina* (Fig. 58)

24.   Cells transversely compressed with cylindrical, conical or globular processes at angles (blunt in freshwater species); 2 (or 1) apical spines, in filamentous forms, unite adjacent cells; walls usually conspicuously areolate in marine forms (but not in *B. laevis* of fresh waters and marine, which is punctate-striate .... (F, M) *Biddulphia* (Figs. 21-28)

25.   (23.) Cells without, or with inconspicuous intercalary bands, walls smooth .... 26.

25.   Cells with conspicuous intercalary bands .... 27.

26.   Walls thin, without structure .... (M) *Leptocylindrus* (Fig. 40)

26.   Walls thick, punctate or areolate; some with apical teeth or some with keel-like projection at edge ....
      (F, B, M) *Melosira* (Figs. 34-38)

27.   (25.) Girdle bands 2 per cell in the form of false collars .... (M) *Bacteriosira* (Fig. 41)

27.   Girdle bands few to many .... 28.

28.   Valves with numerous spinules on surface .... 29.

28.   Valves lacking spinules; intercalary bands numerous, collar-like or with wedge-shaped ends .... 30.

29. Spinules in a single row .... (M) *Detonula* (Fig. 42)

29. Spinules numerous, in more than a single row ....
(M) *Lauderia* (Fig. 54)

30. (28.) Intercalary bands collar-like...................... (F, B, M)
Melosira (Figs. 34-38)

30. Intercalary bands mostly with wedge-shaped ends .... 31.

31. Valve surface flat, smooth .... (M) *Dactyliosolen* (Fig. 43)

31. Valve surface with an asymmetrical tooth at margin ....
(M) *Guinardia* (Fig. 39)

32. (1). Cells sessile, attached to substrate by gelatinous pads .... 33.

32. Cells free-floating .... 34.

33. Cells with apical lobes and often with spines...............................
(F, <u>M</u>) *Biddulphia* (Figs. 21-28)

33. Cells without lobes or spines .... (M) *Isthmia* (Fig. 33)

34. (32.) Cells with conspicuous long siliceous spines.......... 35.

34. Cells lacking long spines; spinules present or absent; some with short, blunt processes .... 41.

35. Cells elongate cylindrical, with a single stout hollow, apical spine extending parallel to long axis of cell .... 36.

35. Cells with 2 or more apical spines, variously disposed .... 37.

36. Spine central, often with a whorl of spinules at its base; cells about 3-5 times longer than broad .... (M)
Ditylum (Figs. 55, 56)

36. Spine mostly excentric, from opposite sides of each end of cell; lacking spinules; cells much longer than broad .... (F, <u>M</u>) *Rhizosolenia* (Figs. 71-75, 79)

37. Spines 2 (rarely 3) at valve apex .... 38.

37. Spines in whorls at apex, spreading .... 40.

38. Spines shorter than cell, from near center of valve.................
(F, M) *Biddulphia* (Figs. 21-28)

38. Spines arising from margins of valve .... 39.

39. Spines not or only slightly spreading, thus more or less parallel to long axis of cell; girdle bands numerous, scale-like............ (F, M) *Attheya* (Figs. 76, 78)

39. Spines much longer than cells, widely spreading from opposite angles of cells................... (F, M) *Chaetoceros* (Figs. 62-66, 68)

40. (37.) Spines forked; lacking girdle bands........................ (M) *Bacteriastrum* (Figs. 67, 69)

40. Spines not forked; girdle bands numerous, scale-like .... (M) *Corethron* (Fig. 70)

41. (34.) Cells trapezoidal, highly sculptured .... (M) *Isthmia* (Fig. 33)

41. Cells of other shapes .... 42.

42. Valves triangular (to 4-angled) in valve view; walls highly ornamented .... 43.

42. Cells not 3- or 4-angled .... 44.

43. Angles of cells constricted, broadly rounded at apices .... (F, M) *Hydrosira* (Fig. 85)

43. Angles acute with short processes .... (M) *Triceratium* (Fig. 32)

44. (42.) Cells hemispherical; girdle view wedge-shaped; lacking intercalary bands .... (M) *Hemidiscus* (Figs. 13, 14)

44. Cells otherwise, some with intercalary bands .... 45.

45. Cells with long gelatinous threads from valve surfaces .... 46.

45. Cells lacking gelatinous threads; discoid .... 47.

46. One thread from valve center; girdles with intercalary bands .... (F, M) *Thalassiosira* (Figs. 48-51, 80)

46. With 4-9 threads from valve surface; lacking intercalary bands .... (M) *Coscinosira* (Fig. 52)

47. (45.) Cells with mostly 1-4 processes or ocelli .... 48.

47. Valves without short blunt projections, but with or without small marginal spinules .... 50.

48. Wall structure granular or cellular, uniform with reference to processes .... (M) *Eupodiscus* (Figs. 16, 17)

48. Wall structure of striations or plaits, more or less radially arranged, or arranged around processes .... 49.

49. Valves with plumose plaits or granules arranged symmetrically around mostly 2 (1 or 3) processes ...... (M) *Auliscus* (Fig. 15)

49. Valves with striae usually radiate to cell center; processes 2-9 .... (M) *Pseudoauliscus* (Fig. 86)

    50. (47.) Valves with a broad wing-like expansion around margin .... (M) *Planktoniella* (Fig. 31)

    50. Cells lacking such a wing .... 51.

51. Valves with distinct star-like structure, with broad hyaline rays from a hyaline center to margin, outer ends with a minute spine; valves otherwise finely or coarsely areolate .... 52.

51. Valves without star-like structure .... 53.

    52. Rays symmetrical, of equal width; areolations between rays delicate valves circular .... (M) *Asterolampra* (Fig. 20)

    52. Rays asymmetrical, one narrower than the others; valves circular to ovoid .... (M) *Asteromphalus* (Fig. 18)

53. (51.) Valves strongly radially bulged, divided into regularly alternating high and low pie-shaped sectors; central area smooth ...... (M) *Actinoptychus* (Fig. 5)

53. Valves not radially bulged .... 54.

    54. Valves with a smooth eye near edge or with conical processes .... 55.

    54. Valves without marginal eye or conical processes, often with marginal spinules .... 56.

55. Valves each with 1 smooth eye near margin, often with marginal spinules; structure clearly radially punctate, not areolate............... (M) *Actinocyclus* (Fig. 6)

55. Valves with 4 or more conical processes regularly arranged near margin; valves areolate .... (M) *Aulacodiscus* (Fig. 19)

56. (54.) Valve structure very fine; central area distinct, finely striate; chromatophores elongate ...... (M) *Hyalodiscus* (Fig. 10)

    56. Valve structure distinct, chromatophores round, disc- or plate-like .... 57.

57. Valves with circular central area surrounded by radiating ribs or costae (often only striae) .... 58.

57. Valves lacking radiating ribs or costae; central area if present, with irregular outline .... 59.

58. Central area large; areolae lacking; girdle view flat or undulating .... (F, M) *Cyclotella* (Figs. 8, 9, 11)

58. Central area small; with distinct radially arranged areolae between ribs .... (M) *Arachnodiscus* (Fig. 30)

59. (57.) Valves radially (or arcuately, in some marine species) densely punctate or with a pattern of polygonal markings; girdles lacking intercalary bands .... 60.

59. Valves without or with interrupted radial punctae, but lacking polygonal markings; girdles with or without intercalary bands .... 61.

60. Punctae interrupted by hyaline areas; valves with a circlet of marginal teeth .... (F) *Stephanodiscus* (Fig. 7)

60. Punctae uniform throughout, or with polygonal markings; in either case, markings are either radially or arcuately arranged .... (F, M̲) *Coscinodiscus* (Figs. 1-4)

61. (59.) Valves with a few (or no) marginal spinules of unequal size; with a few or less central punctae (from which gelatinous hairs may extrude) and a central pore; otherwise with small interrupted radial punctations; intercalary bands 2-4 .... (F, M̲) *Thalassiosira* (Figs. 48-57, 80)

61. Valves without marginal spinules, but with 4-8 subcentral pores from which gelatinous hairs may extrude; lacking intercalary bands .... (M) *Coscinosira* (Fig. 52)

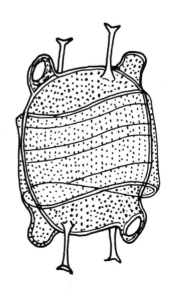

Biddulphia

DIATOMS PENNATE. Valves not centrally constructed, not arranged in relation to a central point but to a median line. Bilaterally symmetrical. Outline generally boat-shaped or rod-shaped, sometimes oval, cuneate, crescent-shaped, or sigmoid; markings generally pinnate or transverse. True raphe, or hyaline median line (pseudoraphe), or raphe obscured by lateral wings or keel always present. Processes such as horns, spines, etc., uncommon. Cell capable of spontaneous movement if a true raphe is present. (Cupp 1943)

1. Plants multicellular, variously colonial in gelatinous secretions (amorphous or tubular), or in a series as filaments (ribbons and chains) or in a zigzag arrangement, or attached to a gelatinous stalks .... 2.

1. Cells solitary (including individual cells of multicellular diatoms .... 55.

    2. Cells stalked .... 3.

    2. Cells without stalks, either in gelatinous secretions, in zigzag series or in filaments (ribbons or chains) .... 14.

3. Cells symmetrical in girdle and valve views in both axes; straight .... 4.

3. Cells asymmetrical, curved (arcuate) in girdle or valve views, or straight and more or less wedge- or club-shaped .... 6.

    4. Valve view with pseudoraphes; stalks short .... (M)
                                       Rhabdonema (Fig. 111)

    4. Valve view with raphes .... 5.

5. Raphe straight, central nodule very elongate.............................
                          (F, M) **Brebissonia** (Fig. 159)

5. Raphe sigmoid, central nodule small .... (F)
                            Achnanthes (Fig. 133)

    6. (3.) Valves with one or both sides curved; dorsal side arcuate.. 7.

    6. Valves straight, but if curved, seen only in girdle view. .... 8.

7. Ventral side flat so both valves are seen at same time.................
                   (F, <u>M</u>) **Amphora** (Fig. 105)

7. Ventral side not flat, both valves more or less arcuate, the cell thus cymbel-form; raphe more or less arcuate ....
                          (F) **Cymbella** (Fig. 113)

8. (6.) Girdle view curved or strongly undulate, bent in middle; valves view straight .... 9.

8. Girdle and valve views straight, cells broader (at least above middle) at one end, in one or both views .... 10.

9. Valve ends of equal width .... (F, M) **Achnanthes** (Figs. 90, 93, 133)

9. Cells broader at one end in both valve and girdle views .... (M) **Rhoicosphenia** (Fig. 115)

10. (8.) Raphe excentric, seen along margins of cell in both valve and girdle views; carinal dots present .... (F, M̲) **Gomphonitzschia** (Fig. 140)

10. Raphe not excentric .... 11.

11. Valves with conspicuous transverse septa .... (M) **Climacosphenia** (Fig. 116)

11. Valves lacking transverse septa .... 12.

12. Valves with raphe only near apex on one, the other valve with a pseudoraphe .... (F) **Peronia** (Fig. 119)

12. Valves with elongate raphes, or with pseudoraphes .... 13.

13. Girdle view smooth; raphes present .... (F̲, M) **Gomphonema** (Figs. 120, 124, 125, 128, 129)

13. Girdle view with 2 bands, with penetrating septa on broader pole; pseudoraphes present .... (M) **Licmophora** (Figs. 117, 123)

14. (2.) Cells in gelatinous secretions, either amorphous matrix or in tubes .... 15.

14. Cells not in tubes or matrix .... 19.

15. Valves more or less sigmoid, as is raphe; striae punctate, both longitudinal and transverse .... (F, M) **Gyrosigma** (Fig. 132)

15. Valves not sigmoid .... 16.

16. Cells highly sculptured, raphe a broad "V" -shape, with concave ventral, and convex or flat dorsal margins .... (F, B) *Epithemia* (Fig. 107)

16. Cells not highly sculptured; either raphes or pseudoraphes present .... 17.

17. Valves with transverse septa, costa-like; girdle with incomplete transverse septa with capitate ends .... (F)
Denticula (Fig. 163)

17. Cells lacking septa; raphes bordered by partially fused siliceous ribs .... 18.

    18. Fused part of ribs elongate in center, branches toward ends 1/3 to 1/6 the valve length ....
(F, B, M) *Amphiplura* (Fig. 160)

    18. Ribs more or less circular in central area, branches about 1/2 the valve length .... (F, B)
Frustulia (Fig. 161)

19. (14.) Cells filamentous, in zigzag series, in ribbons and chains, or in stellate colonies .... 20.

19. Cells filamentous, ribbons or chains or zigzag .... 26.

    20. Cells united more or less uniformly by their broader ends in stellate or spiral colonies, the two ends of cells of different width .... (F, M) *Asterionella*
(Figs. 94-96, 98)

    20. Cells united irregularly, ends of similar width .... 21.

21. Girdle view rectangular, tabular, with incomplete longitudinal or transverse septa .... 22.

21. Cells much longer than broad, lacking septa .... 23.

    22. Cells with a few incomplete longitudinal septa extending well toward cell center .... (F) *Tabellaria*
(Fig. 166, 169)

    22. Cells with many incomplete transverse septa ....
(F) *Tetracyclus* (Fig. 165)

23. (21.) Cells in star-shaped fascicles, spindle-shaped; raphes-contained in excentric keels (seen on opposite sides at 2 different levels of focus) with a row of carinal dots ....
(F, M̲) *Nitzschia* (Figs. 141, 143-147)

23. Cells very long and narrow, girdle view rectangular; valves lacking raphes .... 24.

24. Colonies fan-like or clustered star-like; valves with transverse rows of delicate punctae .... (F, B, M)
Synedra (Figs. 100, 102, 103)

24. Cells in zigzag series; valves with marginal spinules or featureless .... 25.

25. Cell ends unlike .... (M) *Thalassiothrix* (Figs. 97, 99, 101)

25. Cell ends alike .... (M) *Thalassionema* (Fig. 104)

26. (19.) Cells in zigzag series .... 27.

26. Cells united by valves, thus seen in girdle view, forming filaments (ribbons or chains) .... 36.

27. Valves "bone" -shaped with dissimilar ends, one broadly rounded, the other inflated with a retuse to apiculate apex; girdle view elongate wedge-shaped ....
(F) *Actinella* (Fig. 121)

27. Valves otherwise; girdle view rectangular or tabular .... 28.

28. Valves arculate with poles of same size, concave margin a smooth curve, the lower varying from a smooth curve (except for polar inflation) to curved and strongly undulate .... (F) *Eunotia* (Fig. 109, 174)

28. Valves straight .... 29.

29. Cells without girdle vands or septa; valve and girdle views linear to slightly lancet-shaped .... 30.

29. Cells with intercalary bands and/or septa; girdle view rectangular .... 31.

30. Valve ends unlike .... (M) *Thalassiothrix* (Figs. 97, 99, 101)

30. Valve ends similar .... (M) *Thalassionema* (Fig. 104)

31. (29.) Girdle view with numerous intercalary bands, alternating with septa; valves lanceolate .... (M)
Striatella (Fig. 112)

31. Cells otherwise, intercalary bands few or inconspicuous .... 32.

32. Girdle view with longitudinal septa .... 33.

32. Girdle view with transverse costae, septa or false septa extending across valves; lacking longitudinal septa .... 35.

33. Septa rarely extending more than 1/3 the distance to middle of cell, curved at apex .... (F)
Tetracyclus (Fig. 165)

33. Septa extending far toward cell center .... 34.

34. Septa more or less straight; valve view elongate with evident median inflations and slightly inflated poles; girdle view with intercalary bands inconspicuous at ends .... (F) *Tabellaria* (Figs. 166, 169)

34. Septa curved or undulating; intercalary bands 2, one in each half cell .... (M)
Gramatophora (Figs. 167, 168, 172)

35. (32.) Valve view with markedly undulate sides; transverse septa thickened at ends and bent like musical notes. (This is a Centric diatom which resembles Pennate genera.) .... (F, M) *Terpsinoe* (Fig. 29)

35. Valve margins lanceolate to linear; transverse septa uniform, straight .... (F, B) *Diatoma* (Fig. 162)

36. (26). Cells in regular spiraled ribbons in continuing fanshaped arrangement; cells wedge-shaped in both views .... *Meridion* (Fig. 118)

36. Filaments curved or twisted, but not fan-like .... 37.

37. Cells adjoined in curved filaments like a section of a barrel .... (M) *Pseudoeunotia* (Fig. 89)

37. Filaments appearing otherwise, cells in band-like chains or ribbons .... 39.

39. Cells with axial area (median line) ....

39. Cells straight, not sigmoid .... 42.

40. Cells twisted, with sigmoid median line; girdle bands numerous, sigmoid .... (F, B, M) *Amphiprora* (Figs. 175, 176)

40. Cells not sigmoid, but curved along the long axis .... 41.

41. Cells strongly bent, with broadly rounded ends; valve view withsigmoid raphe .... (F, M)
Achnanthes (Fig. 90, 93, 133)

41. Cells moderately curved, with knob-like corners, more or less constricted below ends .... (M)
Campylosira (Fig. 91)

42. (39.) Cells with conspicuous longitudinal or transverse septa .... 43.

42. Cells lacking conspicuous septa .... 47.

43. Girdle view with conspicuous complete, or incomplete longitudinal septa .... 44.

43. Girdle view with transverse septa, complete or incomplete .... 46.

44. Septa 2, running full length of cell ....
(F) *Diatomella* (Fig. 164)

44. Septa more than two, incomplete .... 45.

45. Septa straight .... (F) *Tabellaria* (Figs. 166, 169)

45. Septa curved .... (F) *Tetracyclus* (Fig. 165)

46. (43.) Septa uniform in width, extending to girdle bands ....
(F, B) *Diatoma* (Fig. 163)

46. Septa capitate, extending about to juction of valve and girdle .... (F) *Denticula* (Fig. 163)

47. (42.) Filaments with irregular margins (living cells move relative to each other, in a highly animated fashion; cells very long and slender ....(F, B, M)
Nitzschia paradoxa (Fig. 141)

47. Margins of filaments parallel .... 48.

48. Girdle view with numerous intercalary bands, open at one end, on the other with shorter or longer shallow septa .... (M) *Striatella* (Fig. 112)

48. Cells lacking intercalary bands or septa .... 49.

49. Girdle view with swollen cells united in midregion and tapering to truncate ends which are free ....
(F, B, M) *Fragilaria* (Figs. 87, 88, 170)

49. Girdle view rectangular .... 50.

50. Filament thickened in midregion (like a keel extending length of filament), or uniformly arched from side to side .... 51.

50. Filaments mostly flattened as ribbons .... 52.

    51. Filaments uniformly arched ...... (F) **Hannaea** (Fig. 106)

    51. Filaments much thickened in midregion .... (F, B, M) **Fragilaria** (Figs. 87, 88, 170)

52. (50.) Raphe visible in girdle view .... (F, B, M) **Navicula** (Figs. 153, 156, 157)

52. Raphe lacking; valves with pseudoraphes .... 53.

    53. Cells with sides flat against each other .... (F, M) **Fragilaria** (Figs. 87, 88, 170)

    53. Cells more or less constricted below apex .... 54.

54. Valve view with hyaline central area .... (M) **Plagiogramma** (Fig. 92)

54. Valve view without hyaline central area .... (M) **Dimerogramma** (Fig. 171)

    55. (1.) Cells radially branched, the 3 rays at more or less equal angles from a common center .... (F) **Centronella** (Fig. 86)

    55. Cells unbranched .... 56.

56. Cells saddle-shaped, valve view circular in outline .... (F, M) **Campylodiscus** (Fig. 179)

56. Cells otherwise .... 57.

    57. Cells linear, straight, the ends of different size and shape; cells not wedge- or club-shaped, however .... 58.

    57. Cells with similar ends .... 59.

58. Cells more or less symmetrical, mostly held together by thicker ends in star-like colonies; valves with pseudoraphes .... (F, M) **Asterionella** (Figs. 94-96, 98)

58. Cells "bone-shaped," one end broadly rounded and the other inflated with a retuse or apiculate apex; valves with pseudoraphe visible at ends only .... (F) **Actinella** (Fig. 121)

59. Cells cymbel-like or arcuate, sigmoid or variously bent or twisted in the middle, or only at ends .... 60.

59. Cells club- or wedge-shaped or other shapes .... 73.

60. Cells strongly bent in girdle view; valves straight, more or less linear lanceolate, with a raphe on one, and a pseudoraphe on the other valve .... (F, M) **Achnanthes** (Figs. 90, 93, 133)

60. Cells otherwise .... 61.

61. Valve face spirally twisted, with marginal keels with raphes, and withconspicuous transverse costae ....
(F, B, M) **Surirella** (Fig. 180)

61. Valves otherwise .... 62.

62. Valves with convex dorsal, and straight or more or less concave ventral margin, one or both of which may be undulate .... 63.

62. Valves otherwise .... 65.

63. Valves with terminal nodule or rostrate apices .... 64.

63. Valves curved, semicircular, with parallel margins; lacking pseudoraphe or terminal nodules ....
(F) **Semiorbis** (Fig. 108)

64. Raphe very short, dorsal margin usually more or less convex, smooth to strongly undulate; ventral margin straight or somewhat concave .... (F, ?) **Eunotia** (Figs. 109, 174)

64. Valves with distinct pseudoraphe near ventral margins, with both margins sinuate-dentate .... (F) **Amphicampa** (Fig. 110)

65. (62.) Cells sigmoid in valve or girdle view .... 66.

65. Cells otherwise, cymbel-form, dorsal margin more or less arched and ventral margin more or less flat to concave; margins smooth .... 68.

66. Valve view with keeled raphes diagonally opposite, centric or excentric with distinct carinal dots .... (F, B, M) **Nitzschia** (Figs. 141, 143-147)

66. Valves without keeled raphes, the raphe sigmoid along long axis; striae very difficult to see .... 67.

67. Striae crossing each other in longitudinal and transverse rows .... (F, B, M) *Gyrosigma* (Fig. 132)

67. Striae longitudinal and transverse as well as crossing obliquely .... (F, M) *Pleurosigma* (Figs. 135, 138)

68. Valves kidney-, sickle-, or bracket-shaped; with keeled raphe hardly visible, lying on a ridge on dorsal side of valve .... (F) *Rhopalodia* (Fig. 114)

68. Valves otherwise, with more or less arched dorsal, and with more or less concave or straight ventral margin .... 69.

69. Cells mostly in filamentous bands .... 70.

69. Cells solitary or filamentous.. 71.

70. Filaments curved like sections of a barrel; valves with transverse ribs, punctate between; not constricted near apex .... (M) *Pseudoeunotia* (Fig. 89)

70. Filaments not thus curved; valves areolated, sparsely punctate, constricted near apex ...... (F, M) *Campylosira* (Fig. 91)

71. (69) Valves with central area V-shaped between poles on concave side; transverse septa numerous with 2 or more transverse rows of large punctae between .... (F, B) *Epithemia* (Fig. 107)

71. Valves without V-shaped central area, lacking transverse septa .... 72.

72. Ventral valve flat, with straight or arcuate raphe which is either central to strongly excentric; girdle view rectangular .... (F, ?) *Cymbella* (Fig. 113)

72. Ventral valve somewhat convex; raphe straight, arched or sinuous, strongly excentric lying toward concave side; girdle view often inflated or constricted, the two raphes visible in the same plane .... (F, M) *Amphora* (Fig. 105)

73. (59.) Cells wedge- or club-shaped in either girdle or valve views .... 74.

73. Cells not wedge- or club-shaped but symmetrical, elongate, mostly linear to lanceolate, or swollen in midregion .... 82.

74. Cells curved in girdle view along the long axis, straight in valve view with 2 longitudinal septa parallel to valve face .... (F) *Rhoicosphenia* (Fig. 115)

74. Cells straight in girdle and valve views .... 75.

75. Cells with conspicuous septa; valves without raphes .... 76.

75. Cells otherwise; valves with raphes .... 78.

76. Girdle view with transverse septa appearing as costae; cells usually in fan-shaped colonies .... (M) *Meridion* (Fig. 118)

76. Cells otherwise .... 77.

77. Cells with longitudinal septa at broad end; without internal transverse septa .... (M) *Licmophora* (Figs. 117, 123)

77. Cells without longitudinal septa; valve view with internal transverse septa giving a step-ladder appearance, compartmented .... (M) *Climacosphenia* (Fig. 116)

78. Valves with raphe excentric, seen on opposite sides at two different levels, and with carinal dots .... (F, M) *Gomphonitzschia* (Fig. 140)

78. Raphe otherwise .... 79.

79. Valves with raphe on one valve only, near terminal nodule (not extending the length of the valve), the other valve with a pseudoraphe; cell margins more or less parallel ...... (F) *Peronia* (Fig. 119)

79. Raphe central, complete on both valves; cells with one end broader than the other, straight or more or less swollen in midregion .... 80.

80. Valves with a lateral ("shadow") line parallel to each margin (F) *Gomphoneis* (Fig. 127)

80. Values without such lines .... 81.

81. Valves with large central area, with 2-5 pores on one side of central nodule; raphe filamentous with large terminal fissures turned away from side that has the pores in central area; striae irregularly shortened about central area .... (F) *Didymosphenia* (Fig. 171)

81. Valves differing in above details, otherwise similar; axial field often with one or more isolated and asymmetrically disposed pores, raphe not curved in relation to them ...... (F, M) *Gomphonema* (Figs. 120, 124, 125, 128, 129)

82. Cells with conspicuous costae or septa, with or without raphes or pseudoraphes .... 83.

82. Cells lacking conspicuous septa; with raphes, and/or pseudoraphes .... 94.

    83. Cells with conspicuous costae; septa present or not .... 84.

    83. Cells with conspicuous septa, or septa-like intercalary bands .... 87.

84. Cells egg-shaped (or elongate club-shaped); girdle view with costae extending from margins to girdles, or separated by a girdle band .... (F, B, M) *Opephora* (Fig. 122)

84. Cells otherwise .... 85.

    85. Valves flat or undulate (or spirally twisted), linear, elliptical or ovate with broadly rounded poles; raphes axial or in marginal keels .... 86.

    85. Valves transversely undulate, often somewhat constricted in middle .... (F) *Cymatopleura* (Fig. 177)

86. Valves flat, linear to elliptical, raphes central, axial .... (F) *Pinnularia* (Fig. 155)

86. Valves linear, elliptical or ovate, flat or spirally twisted; raphes in marginal keels .... (F, B, M) *Surirella* (Fig. 180)

    87. Valves with septa-like intercalary bands forming rows of compartments just below valve surface along cell margins (F, B, M) *Mastogloia* (Fig. 173)

    87. Valves lacking such compartments .... 88.

88. Girdle view with conspicuous longitudinal septa .... 89.

88. Girdle view with conspicuous transverse septa .... 93.

    89. Septa incomplete .... 90.

    89. Girdle view with septa complete, 2 running full length of cell .... 92.

90. Septa opposite, strongly curved to "?" -like .... (M) *Grammatophora* (Figs. 167, 168, 172)

90. Septa straight or only slightly curved or bent .... 91.

91. Septa straight, extending well toward cell center .... (F)
    Tabellaria (Figs. 166, 169)

91. Septa somewhat curved, rarely extending to cell center ..
    (F) *Tetracyclus* (Fig. 165)

92. (89.) Valve view with septa appearing as 3 or more or less circular
    compartments .... (F) *Diatomella* (Fig. 164)

92. Valve view transversely striate beneath which along each margin
    are narrow rows of compartments (septa with intercalary bands)
    .... (F, B, M) *Mastogloia* (Fig. 173)

93. (88). Septa uniform, extending to girdle bands ....
    (F, B) *Diatoma* (Fig. 162)

93. Septa capitate, extending to junction of valve and girdle
    (F) *Denticula* (Fig. 163)

94. (82.) Cells elliptical with a raphe on 1 valve, and a pseudoraphe
    on the other .... (F, M) *Cocconeis* (Fig. 131)

94. Cells elliptical or linear, with either raphes or pseud-
    oraphes.. 95.

95. Valve view with pseudoraphe; lacking raphes .... 96.

95. Cells with raphes .... 102.

96. Girdle view with numerous inconspicuous intercalary bands
    or false septa.. 97.

96. Cells not as above. .... 98.

97. Girdle view with numerous intercalary bands and inconspic-
    uous alternate septa.. (M)
    Striatella (Fig. 112)

97. Girdle view with numerous false septa...........................
    (M) *Rhabdonema* (Fig. 111)

98. (96.) Cell ornamentation of regular longitudinal rows of
    punctae and areolae; typically filamentous .... (M)
    Plagiogramma (Fig. 92)

98. Cell ornamentation otherwise, with delicate striae or none;
    valve view narrow linear .... 99.

99. Cell margin with numerous spinules................................ 100.

99. Cells without spinules; not, or only with difficulty, separable
    as solitary cells.. 101.

100. Cell ends alike .... (M) *Thalassionema* (Fig. 104)

100. Cell ends unlike............. (M) *Thalassiothrix* (Figs. 97, 99, 101)

101. (99.) Cells filamentous........................ (F, B, M) *Fragilaria*
(Figs. 87, 88, 170)

101. Cells not filamentous........................... (F, B, M) *Synedra*
(Figs. 100, 102, 103)

102. (95.) Raphes sigmoid or spiralled .... 103.

102. Raphes otherwise, associated with centric or excentric keels
or not .... 104.

103. Valves straight or highly arched, linear elliptical, with a
distinct sigmoid axial field and raphe .... (B, M)
Scoliopleura (Fig. 134)

103. Valves fusiform with 2-3 canal raphes spirally arranged and
with carinal dots .... (F) *Cylindrotheca* (Fig. 139)

104. (102.) Raphes associated with keels .... 105.

104. Raphes axial, not in keels, striae mostly transverse............... 107.

105. Median line straight, not sigmoid, on a centric or excentric keel, raphe at ends of keel; cells usually with a wing or
longitudinal band on one or both sides................................
(B, M) *Plagiotropis* (Figs. 136, 137)

105. Raphe and cell shape otherwise; keels with regularly
arranged carinal dots.. 106.

106. Valves with raphes diagonally opposite ...... (F, B, M) *Nitzschia*
(Figs. 141, 143-147)

106. Valves with raphes opposite each other .... (F, M) *Hantzschia*
(Fig. 142)

107. (104.) Striae crossed or interrupted by 2 to several
longitudinal lines or ribs... 108.

107. Striae not interrupted .... 111.

108. Valves with marginal ridges or furrows, striae distinctly
punctate.. (F) *Neidium* (Fig. 148)

108. Valves otherwise .... 109.

109. Striae not distinct .... (F) *Anomoeoneis* (Fig. 149)

109. Striae costae-like... 110.

110. Striae crossed by 1 or more narrow longitudinal lines near valve
margin .... (F, M) *Caloneis* (Fig. 150)

110. Striae divided into segments by one or more siliceous ribs
.... (B, M) *Oestrupia* (Fig. 154)

111. (107.)   Raphe enclosed between 2 longitudinal ribs; central area not thickened into a stauros .... 112.

111.   Raphe not between 2 longitudinal ribs; central area thickened into a stauros .... 116.

112.   Valves linear elliptical or more or less constricted in mid region; central nodule thickened "H"-shaped; with transverse costae crossed by a longitudinal canal on each side of valve .... (F, M) **Diploneis** (Fig. 130)

112.   Valves linear lanceolate, transverse costae or striae not crossed by longitudinal canals; central nodule not "H"-shaped .... 113.

113.   Raphe very short, central area linear; if raphe is longer, central area of irregular width .... (F, B, M) **Amphipleura** (Fig. 160)

113.   Raphe extending the whole length (or almost) length of valve .... 114.

114.   Valves with transverse costae .... (F, B, M)   **Brebissonia** (Fig. 159)

114.   Valves with transverse striae .... 115.

115.   Terminal nodule rounded or like a pencil point, central nodule not differentiated .... (F, B) **Frustulia** (Fig. 161)

115.   Terminal nodule not so shaped; central nodule appearing as a dark spot surrounded by a bright ring .... (B)   **Frickia** (Fig. 158)

116.   (111.)   Central stauros smooth, spreading to margins of valves and appearing like a cross ...... (F, B, M) **Stauroneis** (Fig. 151)

116.   Stauros interrupted by a few striae, bifid, forming an "X" across face .... (F) **Capartogramma** (Fig. 152)

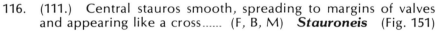

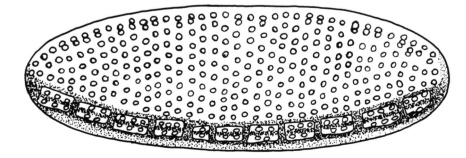

Nitzschia

Descriptions of Genera

Achnanthes Bory. (Centric) (=**Eucocconeis** Cleve, p.p.)
Cells solitary or filamentous, often stalked. Valves linear lanceolate seldom elliptical, one with a raphe, the other with a pseudoraphe; raphe straight or sigmoid *(A. flexella* Kütz. Cleve), lacking nodules; striae of rows (or doubled) of punctae; seldom with strong ribs between rows of striae, or entire cell areolated. Girdle view generally rectangular but more or less strongly bent, "U" or "V" shaped. Differing from **Cocconeis** by absence of loculiferous rim.

HABITAT: freshwater.
A. flexella (Kützing) Cleave. Fig. 133 *(freshwater)*.
A. inflata. Kützing. Fig. 90 *(freshwater).*
A. longipes Agardh. Fig. 93 *(marine).*

Actinella Lewis. (Pennate)
Cells single, filamentous or in zigzag chains. Valves "bone-shaped," linear with dissimilar ends, one broadly rounded and the other inflated with a retuse to apicate apex; sides smooth (except for polar inflations) or undulate. Girdle view elongate-wedge-shaped; striae transverse, next to lateral margins only.
HABITAT: freshwater; mostly in bogs.
A. punctata Lewis. Fig. 121

Actinocyclus Ehrenberg. (Centric)
Cells single, disk-shaped. Valves orbicular, elliptic or rhomboidal-oblong, convex, with a marginal or submarginal pseudo-nodule, often with marginal or submarginal spinules; puncta in radiating rows of unequal length, leaving subulate hyaline spaces between.
HABITAT: marine plankton.
A. ehrenbergii Ralfs. Fig. 6

Actinoptychus Ehrenberg. (Centric)
Cells solitary, disk-shaped. Valves divided into sectors alternately depressed and raised, central area smooth; margin often with numerous spinules. Girdle view lacking girdle bands. Wall usually of several layers.
HABITAT: marine, neritic; often in the plankton.
A. undulatus (Bailey) Ralfs. Fig. 5

Amphicampa Ehrenberg. (Pennate)
Cells solitary. Valves with convex dorsal and straight or slightly concave ventral margins; both margins with 3-6 sinuous dentations; pseudoraphe distinct near ventral margin; apices rostrate.
HABITAT: bogs and ponds; freshwater.
A. eruca Ehrenberg. Fig. 110

Amphipleura Kützing. (Pennate)
Cells solitary, free, in gelatinous masses, or in tubes. Valves broadly fusiform with obtusely rounded ends or narrow, elongate to linear lance-shaped; with a thick silicious rib in apical axis, bifurcate toward each apex ending in a nodule, the raphe between the bifurcations, each branch 1/3 to 1/6 valve length; transverse striae of fine punctae in longitudinal lines, or indistinct. Compare with **Frustulia.**
HABITAT: freshwater, brackish or marine; mostly hard or more or less brackish waters.
A. *pellucida* Kützing. Fig. 160.

Amphiprora (Ehrenberg) Cleve. (Pennate)
(= **Entomoneis** Ehrenb.)
Cells solitary, in ribbons or in gelatinous matrix. Valves lanceolate, convex, with raphe in a keel which is slightly or distinctly sigmoid; striae transversely punctate. Girdle view hour-glass shaped with several straight or sigmoid intercalary bands ornamented with parallel striae or rows of punctae.
HABITAT: fresh- but mostly brackish water and marine.
A. *gigantea* var. *sulcata* (O'Meara) Cleve, Fig. 176. *(marine)*
A. *ornate* Bailey. Fig. 175. *(freshwater)*

Amphora Ehrenberg. (Pennate)
Cells solitary or sessile with concave face on substrate, oval, oblong, elliptic-oval, or sub-quadrangular. Valves cymbelliform, central nodule marginal or submarginal, often dilated into a stauros; raphe often inflated. Girdle view often inflated or constricted, connecting zone striate, plicate or punctate.
HABITAT: freshwater or marine.
A. *ovalis* Kützing. Fig. 105.

Anomoeoneis Pfitzer. (Pennate)
Cells solitary. Valves lanceolate, symmetrical in transverse and longitudinal axes; raphe straight, ends straight or curving; striae punctate, arranged transversely and spaced so as to form longitudinal or oblique hyaline lines which appear undulate or zigzag; central area symmetrical, asymmetrical or unilaterally broad.
HABITAT: freshwater.
A. *sphaerophora* (Kützing) Cleve. Fig. 149.

Arachnodiscus Ehrenberg. (Centric)
Cells solitary disk-shaped with circular outline and almost flat valves, slightly concave in center. Valves with a circular central area and with a strong framework of spokelike ribs or rays on the inside which run from margin toward the center ending a short distance from center and are joined together by a fine membrane; between main rays are more or less short marginal ribs, the shortest forming a chambered ring along valve margin; the delicate network of tangential and radial thickenings or ribs

in connection with larger ribs give valve the appearance of a spider web; unthickened parts of membrane, areolae, appear to be more or less pore-like.
HABITAT: marine; epiphytic on algae and often in plankton.
A. ehrenbergii Bailey. Fig. 30.

Asterionella Hassal. (Pennate)
Cells colonial, star-like or spiral, ends distinctly disimilar, held together by the thicker ends. Valves with median pseudoraphe.
HABITAT: freshwater and marine plankton.
A. formosa Hassal. Fig. 94. *(freshwater)*
A. japponica Cleve. Figs. 95, 96. *(marine)*
A. kariana Grunow. Fig. 98. *(marine)*

Asterolampra Ehrenberg. (Centric)
Cells solitary, disk-shaped, sharply divided into sectors by broad hyaline rays, rays all of same width and tapering to margin; hyaline center divided into more or less wedge-shaped sectors; spines at ends of rays on margin and with fine areolations between.
HABITAT: marine plankton.
A. marylandica Ehrenberg. Fig. 20.

Asteromphalus Ehrenberg. (Centric)
Cells solitary, disk-shaped with circular or slightly ovoid outline. Valves flat with radial undulations, areolated with central smooth area and smooth rays radiating to margin, one ray narrower than others. Girdle view with undulating girdle zone following rays and depressions between them.
HABITAT: marine plankton.
A. heptactis (Brébbison) Ralfs. Fig. 18.

Attheya T. West. (Centric)
Cells solitary or of short filaments, markedly flattened with many intercalary bands. Girdle view rectangular with each angle continued in a long spine-like horn; some species with additional horn midway between the two at poles of valve. Walls only slightly silicified and without markings on valves so lintercalary bands.
HABITAT: freshwater, but mostly marine.
A. zachariasi J. Brun. Fig. 78.
A. decora West. Fig. 76.

Aulacodiscus Ehrenberg. (Centric)
Cells solitary, discoid or box-shaped. Valves with circular outline, flat or slightly lower in middle, with 4 or more conical projections arranged near margin; areolated. Girdle view with intercalary bands.
HABITAT: marine plankton.
A. kittoni Arnott. Fig. 19 (redrawn from Cupp Photomicrograph)

Auliscus Ehrenberg. (Centric)
Cells solitary, cylindrical or discoid. Valves with rays either plumose plaits or with granules arranged around 2 (1 or 3) mastoid processes (ocelli), rarely obscure; sometimes with a subquadrate central portion or sometimes with a radiant cellulation interrupted by a linear series terminating in the ocelli.
HABITAT: marine plankton.
A. sculptus (W. Smith) Ralfs, Fig. 15.

Bacteriastrum Shadbolt. (Centric)
Cells filamentous by fusion of more or less numerous setae regularly arranged around margin of cells; setae of two adjacent cells fused for a certain distance beyond base, farther out divided again. Terminal setae different from others, often curved, not fused and therefore not bifurcating. Girdle view mostly without intercalary bands. Wall delicate, hyaline, without visible structure.
HABITAT: marine plankton.
B. delicatulum Cleve. Figs. 67, 69.

Bacteriosira Gran. (Centric)
Cells cylindrical, in compact filaments by fused valve surfaces in direct contact except at center which is slightly depressed. Valves with a row of minute spinules, marginal, but without appendices. Girdle view with two girdle bands per cell, in the form of false collars.
HABITAT: Arctic marine plankton.
B. fragilis Gran. Fig. 41.

Bellarochia van Heurck. (Centric)
Cells filamentous, long and narrow, scarcely siliceous; with elliptical openings between central and terminal contacts. Valves tri- or quadrangular, with margins unequal, deeply excavated, undulate, with apices slightly raised into a not very robust process. Walls unornamented.
HABITAT: marine plankton.
B. malleus (Brightwell) van Heurck, Figs. 44, 45.

Biddulphia Gray. (Centric)
Cells solitary, filamentous or in zigzag chains, box-shaped to cylindrical. Valve elliptical with 2 angles (or 3- or 4-sided; rarely 5), with shorter or longer horns at apical ends or at corners. Girdle view cylindrical or prism-shaped, with numerous cross striations. Walls strongly siliceous, with very fine slime pores on angles secreting slime cushions.
HABITAT: freshwater (only *B. laevis* Ehrenberg), or marine.
B. aurita (Lyngbye) Brebisson & Godey. Figs. 21, 22, 24. *(marine)*.
B. laevis Ehrenberg. Figs. 23, 25, *(freshwater)*.
B. longicruris Greville. Figs. 27, 28, *(marine)*.
B. longicruris var *hyalina*. (Schröder) Cupp. Fig. 26. *(marine)*.

Brebissonia Grunow. (Pennate)
Cells solitary or borne on long dichotomously branching stalks. Valves rhomboidal-lanceolate with acutely rounded or subrostrate apices; raphe straight, lying between inconspicuous longitudinal ridges; either side of axial field with diagonal punctate striae. Girdle view with rectangular ends and somewhat concave or convex sides, with usually several smooth intercalary bands between highly ornamented girdles.
HABITAT: freshwater or mostly brackish.
B. boeckii (Kützing) Grunow. Fig. 159.

Caloneis Cleve. (Pennate)
Cell solitary, free. Valves of variable shape, usually linear lanceolate to elliptical, symmetrical; striae costa-like and chambered, crossed by one or more longitudinal lines or bands near margin of valve. Girdle view lacking intercalary bands or septa.
HABITAT: freshwater, bracking or marine.
C. amphisbaena (Bory) Cleve. Fig. 150.

Campylodiscus Ehrenberg. (Pennate)
Cells solitary, free, saddle-shaped. Valves circular, with usually short costae, outline perfectly circular appearing irregular because of its curvature, with median lines of the two valves crossing one another at right angles.
HABITAT: freshwater, brackish and marine.
C. hibernicus Ehrenberg. Fig. 179. *(freshwater)*

Campylosira Grunow. (Pennate)
Cells filamentous, cymbelliform, connected by delicate plates with numerous ribs (crown of spines); body curved, 1 valve convex the other concave. Valves areolate, sparsely punctate, lacking a central field. Girdle view arcuate, constricted near apices.
HABITAT: marine plankton.
C. cymbelliformis (A. Schmidt) Grunow. Fig. 91.

Capartogramma Kuff. (Pennate)
Valves symmetrical, generally lanceolate to lunate with or without produced ends; stauros bifid, forming an "X" across valve face; axial area narrowly linear, raphe straight, filamentous.
HABITAT: Epiphytic on *Chara* in fresh water (Merrimac River in New England.)
C. crucicula (Grun. ex Cleve) Ross. Fig. 152.

Centronella M. Voigt. (Pennate)
Cells solitary, valve view 3-rayed, star-shaped, the arms long and narrow, regularly at 120°; with pronounced transverse striae and a fine pseudoraphe. Girdle view lacking intercalary bands or septa, very narrow linear, each arm similar to ***Synedra.***
HABITAT: freshwater.
C. reichelti M. Voigt. Fig. 86.

Ceratulina H. Péragallo. (Centric)

Cells cylindrical, usually in chains. Valves slightly arched with two blunt projections or processes near their margin, attached to adjacent cell by means of a fine, small curved, hair-like process which fits into valve of adjacent cell. Girdle view with numerous annular intercalary bands. Wall weakly siliceous, collapsing when dried; sculpturing very delicate.

HABITAT: marine plankton.

C. bergonii H. Péragallo. Fig. 58.

Chaetoceros Ehrenberg. (Centric)

Cells solitary or mostly filamentous, held together by fusion of setae at opposite valve corners, usually with small apertures between cells. Valves with more or less flat end surface (valve surface) and a cylindrical part (valve mantle). Girdle view with 1 or mostly two girdle bands, frequently unequally developed; intercalary bands present in some but difficult to see. With the greatest number of species of true planktonic marine diatoms. Occuring inland in more or less brackish lakes: Devils L., N. Dakota; Pyramid L., Nevada; Grand Coullee Lakes, Washington; and in some Saskatchewan lakes.

HABITAT: fresh?, brackish, and marine plankton.

C. didymus Ehrenberg. Fig. 64. *(marine).*

C. elmorei Boyer. Fig. 63. *(brackish inland lakes)*

C. galvestonensis Collier & Murphy. Fig.68. *(marine).*

C. gracilis Schütt. Fig. 66. *(marine).*

C. radicans Schütt. Fig. 62. *(marine).*

Climacodium Grunow. (Centric)

Cells more or less "H"-shaped, straight, but usually forming twisted filaments, the apertures between resulting from opposite projections are oval or squarish-oblong. Girdle view lacking intercalary bands. Wall weakly silicious, without visible sculpturing.

HABITAT: marine planktonic.

C. frauenfeldianum Grunow. Fig. 84.

Climacosphenia Ehrenberg. (Pennate)

Cells club- to wedge-shaped. Valves with fine transverse striae which converge, therefore no pseudoraphe; internal septa pierced by row of large oval openings which give a stepladder appearance. Girdle view with two intercalary bands.

HABITAT: marine, attached, or planktonic.

C. moniligera Ehrenberg. Fig. 116.

Cocconeis Ehrenberg. (Pennate)

Cells solitary, epiphytic appressed to substrate, or planktonic when freed. Valves elliptical lacking produced or protracted and distinct ends; pseudoraph valve more or less convex (lower, attached valve),

raphe-bearing valve convex to more nearly flat; opposite valves with different striae pattern and/or structure; raphe valve with a marginal and/or sub-marginal hyalin area or ring, some with a highly refractive band around margin; length usually twice the width.
HABITAT: freshwater or marine.
C. *placentula* Ehrenberg. Fig. 131.

Corethron Castracane. (Centric)
Cells solitary, cylindrical with rounded valves bearing a crown of long thin spines or setae at margin directed outward at an angle. Girdle view with numerous intercalary bands, scale-like, very indistinct. Wall weakly siliceous.
HABITAT: marine plankton.
C. *hystrix* Hensen, Fig. 70.

Coscinodiscus Ehrenberg. (Centric)
Cells solitary, disk- or box-shaped, shorter than broad. Valves mostly circular, with ornamentation of fine punctae radially arranged (without radial hyaline areas) or hexagonal arolae arranged in various ways radial or in curved rows across valve; center smooth or sculptured; with or without spinulae on margins; apiculae 1 or 2 or absent; surface flat, slightly or much rounded, the center flat or depressed. Girdle view with a single girdle band to each valve or with one or more collar-like intercalary bands; Length equal to or less than width.
HABITAT: freshwater (few) or marine planktonic or benthic.
C. *granii* Gough. Fig. 3. *(marine).*
C. *lacustris* Grunow. Fig. 1. *(freshwater).*
C. *lineatus* Ehrenberg. Fig. 2. *(marine).*
C. *radiatus* Ehrenberg. Fig. 4. *(marine).*

Coscinosira Gran. (Centric)
Cells drum-shaped to short cylindrical, filamentous. Valves flat or convex united in loose chains by 4-9 gelatinous threads usually of considerable length; surface with more or less large arolae; margins with or without spinulae or unpaired marginal spines. Girdle view with usually distinct intercalary bands. Similar to **Thalassiosira** with but a single thread connecting cells.
HABITAT: marine plankton, characteristically Arctic.
C. *polychorda* Gran. Fig. 52.

Cyclotella Kützing. (Centric)
Cells drum-shaped, discoid; mostly solitary but some in short straight or spiral chains. Valves circular with two concentric regions: an inner, smooth (or finely punctae), and an outer with radial striae or punctae. Girdle view smooth with or without intercalary bands.
HABITAT: freshwater, mostly planktonic.
C. *antique* W. Smith. Fig. 9.

C. bodanica Eulenst. Fig. 11.
C. meneghiniana Krieger. Fig. 8.

Cylindrotheca Rabenhorst. (Centric)
Cells solitary, fusiform, with 2-3 raphe canals arranged spirally and showing juxtaposition; carinal dots present. Walls little silicified, almost invisible in water mounts.
HABITAT: freshwater (rare).
C. gracilis (Brebbison) Grunow. Fig. 139.

Cymatopleura W. Smith. (Pennate)
Cells solitary. Valves elliptical, naviculoid or linear (or constricted); raphe contained in marginal canal; surface transversely undulate, finely striate showing several transverse bands appearing shaded, with distinct (or inconspicuous) pseudoraphe.
HABITAT: freshwater, planktonic.
C. solea (Brebbison) W. Smith. Fig. 177.

Cymbella Agardh. (Pennate)
Cells solitary, stalked or in tubes. Valves asymmetrical, mostly lunate (or semicircular but with some degree of concave dorsiventrality), subnaviculate or subrhombic; concave side a smooth curve or slightly swollen in middle; surface flat; raphe straight or arcuate, either almost central or strongly eccentric; with dots occasionally in central area, 1 to several subtile or quite distinct; ornamentation always somewhat radiate, of either striae or rows of punctae. Girdle view rectangular with smooth sides, lacking intercalary bands.
HABITAT: mostly freshwater; brackish.
C. aspera (Ehrenberg) Cleve. Fig. 113.

Dactyliosolen Castracane. (Centric)
Cells cylindrical, single or in long closed chains by flat valve surface. Valves circular, smooth, margins sometimes with indistinct little nodules. Girdle view with numerous intercalary bands, half-collar-shaped, with somewhat spirally twisted, wedge-shaped ends fitting together in a tooth-like manner. Mantle surface with fine or coarse areolae.
HABITAT: marine plankton.
D. antarcticus Castracane. Fig. 43.

Denticula Kützing. (Pennate)
Cells single, in short loose chains or in gelatinous masses. Valves elongate, symmetrical, linear, lanceolate or elliptical; with almost wholly concealed keel next to one margin within a straight raphe with small central and polar nodules; internal to valve face is a series of transverse parallel septa appearing as costae; with 2 longitudinal septa, each with a single large transversely oval perforation between 2 successive

transverse septa. Girdle view with somewhat convex sides and truncate poles; transverse septa with capitate ends extending to juncture of valve and girdle, the ends represent the only portion of the longitudinal septa visible when cells are viewed from this side.

HABITAT: freshwater.

D. pelagica var. intermedia Hustedt. Fig. 163

Detonula Schütt. (Centric)
Cells cylindrical to oblong in compact filaments by valve surfaces. Valves circular with one row of marginal spinules intermeshed with those of adjacent valve; lacking apiculae. Girdle view with numerous intercalary bands in form of false-collars.

HABITAT: Arctic marine plankton.

D. confervacea (Cleve) Gran. Fig. 42.

Diatoma de Candolle. (Pennate)
Cells single, free or sessile, in zigzag chains or filaments. Valves lanceolate or linear, often dilated at apex, with longitudinal septa appearing as costae across valve; pseudoraphe rather indistinct. Girdle view rectangular, quadrate to elongate, with one or more intercalary bands, the transverse septa extending to girdle bands. Similar to **Meridion** with wedge-shaped girdle view, and to **Denticula** with capitate transverse septa in girdle view.

HABITAT: freshwaters (cool, in mountains).

D. vulgare Bory. Fig. 162.

Diatomella Greville. (Pennate)
Cells single, in filaments or zigzag chains. Valve elliptical-lanceolate, somewhat tumid in middle; with marginal striae and large central area; raphe distinct; longitudinal septa appear as a circular perfortion at each pole and one of larger diameter midway between the 2 polar ones. Girdle view rectangular with thickened intercalary bands between girdles and two longitudinal septa extending whole length of cell, each septum with holes, one at each end of valve below median ends of raphe.

HABITAT: freshwater of mountains (Yellowstone National Park).

D. balfouriana Greville. Fig. 164.

Didymosphenia M. Schmidt. (Pennate)
Valves swollen at apex and base, and in the middle portion which is wider than apex or base, a little asymmetrical to apical axis; central area large, with 2-5 large pores on one side of central nodule; raphe filamentous with large terminal fissures turned away from side that has the pores in central area; striae irregularly shortened about the central area. Girdle view wedge-shaped, without intercalary bands or septa.

HABITAT: freshwater (Virginia).

D. geminata M. Schmidt. Fig. 126.

Diploneis Ehrenberg. (Pennate)
Cells solitary, free. Valves linear elliptical or more or less constricted in mid region; central nodule thickened, "H"-shaped, with a more or less broad siliceous rib in apical axis which is bisected by raphe, on outer sides of arms of "H" lies a longitudinal canal of varying breadth on each side of valve, these crossed by costae or more often have poroids or spots arranged in various patterns; transverse costae present throughout valve on marginal side of the longitudinal canal, these about parallel or more or less radiate; between costae are double rows of pores; costae may be crossed by longitudinal ribs, and alveoli may be arranged as to form longitudinal lines.
HABITAT: freshwater and marine.
D. finnica (Ehrenberg) Cleve. Fig. 130.

Dimerogramma Ralfs. (Pennate)
Cells filamentous. Valves navicular, with distinct pseudoraphe and terminal clear space; striae present; lacking a central pseudo-nodule (hyaline space as in **Plagiogramma**).
D. fulrum (Greg) Ralfs. Fig. 171.

Ditylum Bailey. (Centric)
Cells solitary or united in chains; elongated, prism-shaped to cylindrical. Valves angular, 3-4-angled, with long central spines, and with radiant punctae.
HABITAT: marine plankton.
D. brightwellii (West) Grunow. Figs. 55, 56.

Epithemia Brebisson. (Pennate)
Cells solitary, attached to algae by concave face, in gelatinous masses or in loose ribbons. Valves with concave ventral and convex dorsal margin more or less parallel; poles broadly rounded or subcapitate; central area V-shaped, midway between poles on concave side; with numerous transverse septae appearing as costae, between which are two or more transverse rows of large punctae. Girdle view rectangular with smooth girdles and often with intercalary bands.
HABITAT: fresh and brackish waters.
E. argus (Ehrenberg) Kützing. Fig. 107.

Eucampia Ehrenberg. (Centric)
Cells filamentous, united by processes; spirally curved, with large apertures between cells. Valves elliptical with two blunt processes; lacking spines or setae. Girdle view with numerous intercalary bands which are difficult to see in water mounts.
HABITAT: marine plankton.
E. zoodiacus Ehrenberg. Fig. 81.

Eupodiscus Ehrenberg. (Centric)
Cells solitary, disk-shaped. Valves with cellular and granular structure,

without a median area; with 1 to 4 processes not connected with one another. Girdle face narrow.
HABITAT: marine plankton.
E. argus Ehrenberg. Figs. 16, 17. (Species not from North America).

Eunotia (Ehrenberg. (Pennate)
Cells free-floating or epiphytic; and solitary or united by valves in filaments. Valves asymmetrical to longitudinal or apical axis, dorsal margin usually more or less convex, smooth to strongly undulate, ventral margin straight or somewhat concave; raphe short, extending but a small fraction of distance from pole to middle of cell, lacking central nodules. Girdle view rectangular with terminal nodules (lacking in filamentous **Fragilaria**), intercalary bands usually present; lacking costae or septa.
HABITAT: freshwater.
E. pectinalis. (Kützing) Rabenhorst. Fig. 174.
E. robusta Ralfs.

Fragilaria Lyngbye. (Pennate)
Cells filamentous. valves linear to fusiform, bilaterally symmetrical, often with poles attenuated and sides with one or more intercalary bands between girdles. Solitary cells hardly distinguishable from **Synedra** which is not colonial.
HABITAT: freshwater, brackish, and marine plankton.
F. construens (Ehrenberg) Grunow. Fig. 170.
F. crotonensis Kitton. Fig. 87.
F. islandica Grunow. Fig. 88.

Frickia Heid. (Pennate)
Valve linear, a little narrower at broadly rounded ends; terminal nodule of each end of raphe a narrow rib between ends of longitudinal ribs enclosing raphe, which is a simple slit or groove; ends of raphe some distance from ends of valves; central nodule appears as an alongate dark spot surrounded by a bright ring.
HABITAT: brackish water, in southeastern states.
F. lewisiana (Greville) Heid (the only species.) Fig. 158.

Frustulia Agardh. (Pennate)
Cells solitary, free or in gelatinous tubes or matrix. Valves naviculoid (linear elliptic to rhombo-lanceolate); raphe is a groove between siliceous ribs which fuse at terminal nodule, often appearing as a single rib, two ends of rib not connected at central nodule; terminal nodule thickened the shape of a pencil point; striae longitudinal and transverse through most of valve at 90° angle.
Compare with **Amphipleura** and **Frickia.**
HABITAT: fresh and brackish waters.
F. rhomboides (Ehrenberg) De Toni, Fig. 161.

Gomphoneis Cleve. (Pennate)

Similar in shape, structure and striae to ***Gomphonema*** but differing from that genus in having a longitudinal line next to both margins.

HABITAT: fresh water.

G. herculeana (Ehrenberg) Cleve. Fig. 127.

Gomphonema Agardh. (Pennate)

Cells solitary and moving, or on gelatinous stalks or in matrix, transversely asymmetrical in both valve and girdle views. Valves straight, lanceolate or clavate, with one pole capitate or broader than the other, the length from central nodule to apex less than length from central nodule to base, the upper half usually broader than the lower. Girdle view wedge-shaped. Compare with ***Gomphoneis.***

HABITAT: fresh water mostly, and marine.

G. acuminatum Ehrenberg. Fig. 120. *(freshwater).*

G. constricta Ehrenberg. Fig. 128. *(freshwater).*

G. geminatum (Lyngbye) Agardh. Fig. 129. *(freshwater).*

Gomphonitzschia Grunow. (Pennate)

Cells club- or wedge-shaped. Valves club-shaped, the larger end broadly rounded, the lesser attenuate subcapitate; raphe-canal lateral and excentric, with carinal dots as in ***Nitzschia.***

HABITAT: fresh waters.

G. ungeri Grunow. Fig. 140. (Species not from the United States).

Grammatophora Ehrenberg. (Pennate)

Cells in zigzag chains by adherent adjacent angles or in star-like colonies. Valves usually linear, more or less constricted medianally or with parallel sides. Girdle view rectangular with rounded corners; with two intercalary bands, one in each cell half; with two polar, flat or more or undulating to "?" shaped septa running far toward center; mantle with short pseudosepta.

HABITAT: marine.

G. angulosa Ehrenberg. Fig. 167.

G. marina (Lyngbye) Kützing. Figs. 168, 172.

Guinardia H. Péragallo. (Centric)

Cells single or in straight or twisted chains, close-set, cylindrical, elongate, the length greater than width, slightly curved. Valves circular, surface flat with an asymmetrical lateral rudimentary tooth at the valve margin. Girdle view with numerous intercalalry bands which are collar-like or with wedge-shaped ends.

HABITAT: marine plankton.

G. flaccida (Castracane) H. Péragallo. Fig. 39.

Gyrosigma Hassall. (Pennate)

Cells solitary, free (one species in tubes). Valves elongate, linear or lanceolate, slightly to strongly sigmoid; axial area very narrow, central

area small; striae punctate in longitudinal and transverse rows perpendicular to each other.
HABITAT: freshwater, brackish and marine.
G. *spenceri* (Quekett) Cleve. Fig. 132. *(marine).*

Hannaea (Ehrenberg) Patrick. (Pennate)
(=*Ceratoneis* Ehrenberg). Cells solitary or in short bands. Valves curved, with rostrate-capitate apices and with a more or less prominent thickening (pseudonodule) in middle of concave side; with a pseudoraphe girdle view linear with parallel sides and truncate ends.
HABITAT: cool, flowing fresh waters especially in mountains.
H. *arcus* (Ehrenberg) Patrick (the only species). Fig. 106.

Hantzschia Grunow. (Pennate)
Cell shape and structure as in **Nitzschia**, but differing in transverse section being rectangular instead of rhombic, and with keeled marings of a pair of valves lying opposite instead of diagonal to each other.
HABITAT: freshwater, brackish, and marine.
H. *amphioxys* (Ehrenberg) Grunow. Fig. 142. *(freshwater).*

Hemiaulus Ehrenberg. (Centric).
Cells single or in filaments, more or less bent, thus the filaments curved and/or twisted, with large or small rectangular or oval apertures between adjacent cells. Valves elliptical with two narrow pointed polar processes parallel with cell axis, one or more hyaline claws terminating process. Girdle view lacking (apparently)intercalary bands. Wall finer or coarser areolated or punctated.
HABITAT: oceanic or neretic marine plankton.
H. *hauckii* Grunow. Fig. 83.
H. *membranaceous* Cleve. Fig. 82.

Hemidiscus Wallich. (Centric)
Cells solitary. Valves large, semi-lunate, finely striate with small spines on margins from which radiate somewhat more robust striae which are finely punctate and extend to smooth center. Girdle view cuneate.
HABITAT: marine plankton.
H. *cuneiformis* var. *ventricosa* (Castracane) Hustedt. Fig. 14.
H. *hardmanianus* (Greville) Mann. Fig. 13.

Hyalodiscus Ehrenberg. (Centric)
Cells solitary. Valves orbicular, convex like a watch glass, spineless or without elevations; with umbilicate center, which is very finely striate, subhyaline, with rays or decussating lines.
HABITAT: marine plankton, especially in Arctic seas.
H. *subtilis* Bailey. Fig. 10.

Hydrosira Wallich. (Centric)
Cells solitary or in filaments. Valves triangular or compressed,

constricted at angles which are broadly rounded. Girdle view quadrangular, areolate, with connecting membrane finely punctate.
HABITAT: marine plankton.
H. triquetra Wallich. Fig. 85.

Isthmia Agardh. (Centric)
Cells solitary but mostly cohering irregularly to substrate or to other cells, trapezoidal or rhombohedral in shape. Valves elliptical, unlike, unipolar, one pole with blunt or more pointed hump, with or without ribs. Girdle band usually strongly developed. Wall strongly siliceous, with large areolae and chambers, at angles are a group of very small areolae which secrete mucilage.
HABITAT: mostly sessile, becoming marine planktonic.
I. nervosa Kützing. Fig. 33.

Lauderia Cleve. (Centric)
Cells cylindrical, in filaments joined by fine threads, either touching or not. Valves rounded, surface radially striate; with an unpaired, oblique, outwardly directed apiculus on each valve, and with numerous very small spinules or slime canals at margin and over most of surface; center of valve slightly concave. Girdle view with intercalary bands numerous, collar-like, more or less conspicuous; mantle and surface of intercalary bands delicately areolated.
HABITAT: marine plankton.
L. borealis Gran. Fig. 54.

Leptocylindrus Cleve. (Centric)
Cells long cylindrical, filamentous, united by whole flat valve surface. Valves flat, without spines or processes. Girdle view with intercalary bands but very difficult to see. Walls thin, hyaline, without visible sculpture.
HABITAT: marine plankton.
L. danicus Cleve. Fig. 40.

Licmophora Agardh. (Pennate)
Cells wedge- or club-shaped, stalked. Valves narrow and pointed at lower end, the other broader, usually rounded; pseudoraphe usually distinct, often developed as a strong siliceous rib. Girdle view with intercalary bands one of which in each valve pierces the cavity like a septum from above, open below.
HABITAT: littoral marine, attached to substrate.
L. abbreviata Agardh. Figs. 117, 123.

Lithodesmium Ehrenberg. (Centric)
Cells united in long, straight filaments with concealed apertures. Valves three-cornered with marginal membrane by which adjacent cells are joined; with a long, thin, hollow spine in center of valve. Girdle view with collar-like intercalary bands.
HABITAT: marine plankton.
L. undulatum Ehrenberg. Fig. 46.

Mastogloia Thwaites. (Pennate)
Cells solitary, or colonial in gelatinous tubes. Valves elliptical to lanceolate or linear with bluntly rounded to protracted capitate ends; axial area narrow; raphe generally wavy or lateral in some portions of each branch (or filiform and straight); central area generally small, or expanded on both sides to form and "H"- configuration; striate with costae between. Girdle view with intercalary bands with loculi (marginal chambers) present on inner side of band; chambers equal or of varying size in a single band.
HABITAT: mostly marine and brackish; few of fresh waters.
M. smithii var. *abnormis* Grunow. Fig. 173.

Melosira Agardh. (Centric)
Cells cylindrical, elliptical or circular, united in filaments by valve centers. Valves either simply punctate or punctate and areolate. Girdle view with intercalary bands lacking or many and narrow.
HABITAT: freshwater, brackish and marine.
M. binderana Kützing. Fig. 37. *(freshwater).*
M. granulata (Ehrenberg) Ralfs. Fig. 36. *(freshwater).*
M. moniliformis (Müller) Agardh. Fig. 35. *(marine).*
M. sulcata (Ehrenberg) Kutzing. Fig. 38. *(marine).*
M. varians Agardh. Fig. 34. *(freshwater).*

Meridion Agardh. (Pennate)
Cells wedge-shaped, forming free-floating fan-shaped or flat spiraling filaments, joined valve to valve. Valves cuneate, clavate, or obovate and with very delicate transverse striae and an indistinct pseudoraphe; with transverse septa which are costae-like. Girdle view with one or two intercalary bands.
HABITAT: fresh waters.
M. circulare (Greville) Agardh. Fig. 118.

Navicula Bory. (Pennate)
Cells solitary, free. Valves elongate, usually narrowed toward poles and with capitate, rounded or rostrate apices; raphe distinct, axial, straight not bordered by ridges; with well-defined but small central and polar nodules; striae of distinct or indistinct puncta or in some cases costa-like; central area may be broadened, lyre-like.
HABITAT: fresh and brackish mostly; some are marine.
N. distans. (W. Smith) Ralfs. Fig. 157. *(marine).*
N. membranacea Cleve. Fig. 156. *(marine).*
N. mutica Kützing. Fig. 153. *(freshwater).*

Neidium Pfitzer. (Pennate)
Cells solitary, free. Valves linear, linear-lanceolate, elliptical or gibbous and with acute, obtuse, subcapitate or subrostrate poles; axial area and raphe straight; with transverse rows of punctae, these interrupted by two to several longitudinal clear lines. Girdle view

rectangular, lacking intercalary bands. Similar to Caloneis in the longitudinally interrupted transverse striae, but differs in having punctae instead of striae.

HABITAT: exclusively of fresh waters.

N. hitchcockii (Ehrenberg) Cleve. Fig. 148.

Nitzschia Hassall. (Pennate)

Cells solitary or filamentous, of varied outline in valve view: straight or sigmoid; linear to elliptical; with or without middle construction, and with acute, subrostrate or attenuated apices. Next one margin of valve is a keel (in which raphe lies) facing the unkeeled margin of the other valve; raphe with a uniseriate row of "carinal dots" which are circular pores opening to cell's interior; with transverse rows of punctae across valve face. Girdle and valve sides not at right angles to each other, but rhombic instead of rectangular in transverse section. Girdle view elongate, straight or sigmoid, often with ends somewhat attenuated.

HABITAT: freshwater, brackish and marine.

N. bilobata var. *minor* Grunow. Fig. 147. *(marine)*.

N. linearis (Agardh) W. Smith. Fig. 145. *(freshwater)*.

N. longissima (Brebisson) Ralfs. Fig. 146. *(marine)*.

N. paradoxa (Gmelin) Grunow. Fig. 141. *(freshwater, brackish, or marine)*.

N. seriata Cleve. Fig. 144. *(marine)*.

N. sigmoidea (Ehrenberg) W. Smith Fig. 143. *(freshwater)*.

Oestrupia Heid. (Pennate)

Valves strongly convex, linear to lanceolate, with conspicuous longitudinal ribs dividing striae into one or more segments, otherwise similar to **Pinnularia;** raphe sometimes raised well above rest of valve; central area distinct, axial area variable in width on each side of raphe; striae radiate, appearing to be chambered with openings as in **Caloneis** or **Pinnularia.**

HABITAT: brackish or marine. (Known only from New Jersey).

O. powelli (Lewis) Heid. Fig. 154.

Opephora Petit. (Pennate)

Valves egg- or club-shaped, with transverse costae bisected by pseudoraphe. Girdle view wedge-shaped, the costae running down to place where girdles overlap each other, or are separated by an intercalary band.

HABITAT: freshwater, but mostly marine.

O. martyi Heribaud. Fig. 122. *(freshwater)*.

Peronia Brebisson & Arnott. (Pennate)

Valves linear, club-shaped, capitate at one end, with bluntly rounded apices, slightly wider centrally; one valve with a raphe, the other with a pseudoraphe, the raphe apparent only at terminal nodules (not

extending the length of valve). Girdle view wedge-shaped.
HABITAT: freshwater.
P. erinacea Brebisson & Arnott. Fig. 119.

Pinnularia Ehrenberg. (Pennate)
Cells solitary or rarely girdle to girdle in filaments. Valves symmetrical, usually with rounded poles and straight parallel sides, some inflated in middle; axial field broad, sometimes over 1/3 the valve width and often expanded near central and polar nodules; raphe a line or filament variously twisted in some; striae transverse, costae-like chambers opening into interior of valve, the margins ap-pearing to form a band of variable width crossing striae (obscure) in some). Girdle view rectangular with smooth girdles and without intercalary bands.
HABITAT: freshwater.
P. gentilis (Donk) Cleve. Fig. 155.

Plagiogramma Greville. (Pennate)
Cells in close filaments by valves. Valves linear-lanceolate, sometimes with wavy margins; with transapical ribs that penetrate more or less deeply inter inner part of cell as pseudosepta, often only very shallow; usually two pairs of ribs present, one lies near center, the other near end of valve, seldom several ribs present, very seldom only one rib in center. Girdle view rectangular-tabular or constricted below poles, lacking intercalary bands and septa.
HABITAT: marine plankton.
P. vanheurckii Grunow. Fig. 92.

Plagiotropis Pfitzer. (Pennate)
(=**Tropidoneis** Cleve)
Valves similar to **Navicula** but very convex, lance-acute, usually with a wing or longitudinal band on one or both sides, median line straight, not sigmoid, on a centric or excentric keel; striae transverse and longitudinal, punctae. Girdle zone simple.
HABITAT: alkaline fresh waters, brackish and marine.
P. lepidoptera var. *proboscidea* (Cleve) Reimer.
(=*Tropidoneis lepidoptera* var. *proboscidea* Cleve). Figs. 136, 137.

Planktoniella Schütt. (Centric)
Cells disk-shaped, single. Valves with a hyaline wing-like expansion all around consisting of extra-cellular chambers strengthened by radial rays, weakly siliceous, an organ of flotation; wall areolated like those of *Coscinodiscus excentricus.*
HABITAT: marine plankton.
P. sol (Wallich) Schütt. Fig. 31.

Porosira Jörgensen. (Centric)
Cells discoid-cylindrical, united in loose chains by numerous pads of short, thick mucilage. Valves finely areolate with numerous puncta,

(mucilage pores) and one apicula at margin; mucilage bands with 15-20 very fine fibrils which are seen with difficulty. Girdle view with intercalary bands.

HABITAT: mostly Arctic marine plankton.

P. glacialis (Grunow) Jörgensen. Fig. 57. (Redrawn from photomicrograph of Brunel).

Pleurosigma W. Smith (Pennate)
Cells solitary, free. Valves similar to **Gyrosigma** in general outline and with the same sigmoid raphe, but striae differ. In **Pleurosigma** striae are in three series; one parallel to the transverse axis of valve and the two others oblique to the axial field.

HABITAT: freshwater, but mostly brackish or marine.

F. elongatum W. Smith. Fig. 138. *(marine).*

P. hamulifera Brun & Tempere. Fig. 135. *(marine).*

Pseudauliscus Lead-Fort. (Centric)
Cells disk-shaped. Valves round or elliptic, cellular or granular with median hyaline space absent or very small; striations usually radiate; with 2 to 9 processes surrounded by a hyaline zone.

HABITAT: marine plankton.

P. radiatus (Baily) Rattray. Fig. 12. (Atlantic Coast).

Pseudoeunotia Grunow. (Pennate)
Cells united in filaments by valve surfaces, appearing as sections of a barrel. Valves dorsiventral, with strongly arched back margin; surface with thin transapical ribs, the membrane lying between the ribs delicately areolated-punctated; lacking pseudoraphe and central area.

HABITAT: marine plankton.

P. doliolus (Wallich) Grunow. Fig. 89.

Rhabdonema Kützing. (Pennate)
Cells filamentous or in zigzag chains, or solitary and shortly stipitate. Valves lanceolate or linear, with pseudoraphe and smooth apices with costae or striae of robust beads. Girdle view with numerous false septa.

HABITAT: marine plankton.

R. adriaticum Kützing. Fig. 111.

Rhizosolenia Ehrenberg. (Centric)
Cells free-floating, solitary or in straight or twisted filaments. Valve apex terminating in a single centric or excentric spine--usually very long; girdle view elongate with many scale-like intercalary bands.

HABITAT: freshwater and marine plankton.

R. alata fa. *curvirostris* Gran. Fig. 74. *(marine).*

R. eriensis H. L. Smith. Fig. 71. *(freshwater).*

R. robusta Norman. Fig. 75. *(marine).*

R. setigera Brightwell. Fig. 72. *(marine).*

R. stolterfothii H. Péragallo. Fig. 77. *(marine).*

R. stuliformis Brightwell. Fig. 79. *(marine).*

Rhoicosphenia Grunow. (Pennate)
Cells stalked, sessile on algae, or breaking free. Valves oblanceolate, wedge-shaped, epitheca with median pseudoraphe, lateral to it are transverse rows of delicate striae; hypotheca with median raphe and central polar nodules and parallel striae more or less radially disposed with reference to central nodule. Girdle view wedge-shaped, distinctly curved in long axis, intercalary bands present, unornamented; with two longitudinal septa parallel to valve face.
HABITAT: freshwater.
R. curvata (Kützing) Grunow. Fig. 115.

Rhopalodia O. Müller. (Pennate).
Cells solitary, free floating. Valve lunate to reniform, often with convex margin medianly inflated and usually with acute apices; axial field lies next to concave valve margin, visible throughout whole length of valve; slightly keeled on dorsal side, the canal raphe hardly visible lying in the keel which is on a ridge on the dorsal side of valve; with transverse costae, between which one or more delicate striae. Girdle view linear, linear elliptic, or clavate, inflated in the median portion, and with broadly rounded poles; girdle zone unornamented, with or without intercalary bands.
HABITAT: freshwater.
R. gibba (Ehrenberg). O. Müller. Fig. 114.

Schroederella Pavillard. (Centric)
Cells cylindrical, solitary or mostly in filaments. Valves slightly convex, somewhat concave in center, with a distinct spine in depression of center which joins that belonging to adjacent cell; with a marginal row of small spinules from each of which arise two gelatinous threads which diverge and join the corresponding thread of the next cell, thus forming a characteristic zigzag, or sometimes the threads apparently straight. Girdle view with numerous intercalary bands forming incomplete hoops with very small punctae.
HABITAT: marine plankton.
S. delicatula (H. Péragallo) Pavillard. Fig. 53.

Scoliopleura Grunow. (Pennate)
Cells solitary. Valves straight, highly arched, linear elliptical with a distinctly sigmoid axial field and raphe, with rather small central and polar nodules; with transverse or slightly radiate straie or rows of punctae (some species with longitudinal line bordering sides of axial field. Girdle view elliptico-lanceolate with zone of overlap of girdles somewhat sigmoid.
HABITAT: brackish or marine.
S. peisonis Grunow. Fig. 134. (The only species in the United States, from salt marshes bordering Great Salt Lake, Utah).

Semiorbus Patrick. (Pennate)
Cells solitary. Valves curved, semicircular, margins parallel or almost; lacking pseudoraphe, costae and terminal nodules. Girdle view without septa or intercalary bands. Differing from **Amphicampa** by the parallel margins of valve which are without crenulations or undulations; differing from **Eunotia** by lack of terminal nodules.
HABITAT: fresh water bogs and ponds, mostly.
S. hemicyclus (Ehrenberg) Patrick. Fig. 108. (The only species).

Skeletonema Greville. (Centric)
Cells circular, lens-shaped, oblong or cylindrical. Valves circular, somewhat arched, without distinct structure; with a row of fine spines at edge of valve parallel to longitudinal axis; spines interlocking midway between adjacent cells unite them into chains. Cytoplasm of neighboring cells in contact through hollow spines.
HABITAT: marine plankton.
S. costrum (Greville) Cleve. Fig. 59.

Stauroneis Ehrenberg. (Pennate)
Cells solitary. Valves of much the same shape as those of *Navicula*, mostly lanceolate, or small forms elliptical. Valves with narrow but conspicuous axial field with a straight raphe with fairly small polar nodules; central nodule thickened and transversely extended to lateral margins of valve, this "stauros" is the thickened nodule which lacks ornamentation; with slightly radiate parallel striae or rows of punctae. Stauros and axial field divide the ornamentation into four parts, cross-like (G. *staur* = cross).
HABITAT: freshwater and marine.
S. phoenocentron Ehrenberg. Fig. 151.

Stephanodiscus Ehrenberg. (Centric)
Cells discoid or cylindrical, solitary. Valves circular in outline and radially punctae; towards periphery punctae are in multiseriate rows with smooth areas between them; towards the center punctae are uniseriate; with stout, short marginal spine external to each radial smooth area (between rows of punctae). Girdle view smooth, lacking intercalary bands.
HABITAT: freshwater plankton.
S. niagrae Ehrenberg. Fig. 7.

Stephanopyxis Ehrenberg. (Centric)
Cells oblong, oval, or nearly circular, usually in short filaments. Valve margin rounded with a crown of stout spines or hollow needles nearly parallel with pervalvar axis; wall with hexagonal areolations; cytoplasm of adjacent cells in contact through hollow spines. Girdle view lacking intercalary bands.
HABITAT: marine plankton.
S. turris (Greville & Arnott) Ralfs. Fig. 61.
S. palmeriana (Greville) Grunow. Fig. 60.

Streptotheca Shrubsole. (Centric)
Cells filamentous, extremely flat with square outline (some are three-cornered), united by valve faces without or with only small apertures; filaments strongly and regularly twisted. Valves narrowly elliptical with rudimentary central knob. Walls not silicious.
HABITAT: marine plankton.
S. thamensis Shrubsole. Fig. 47.

Striatella Agardh. (Pennate)
Cells in closed filaments or zigzag chains; some on fixed stalks. Valves lanceolate; pseudoraphe oblique or nearly straight; with delicate transapical rows of punctated striae. Girdle view nearly rectangular, tabular; intercalary bands numerous, open on one end, on the other with shorter or longer shallow septa thickened slightly near margin, the thickenings alternating in adjacent intercalary bands; which are striated in pervalvar direction; wall weakly siliceous.
HABITAT: marine, littoral and planktonic.
S. unipunctata (Lyngbye) Agardh. Fig. 112.

Surirella Turpin. (Pennate)
Cells solitary, free. Valve view linear, elliptical or oval, sometimes constricted; surface nearly flat, rarely spirally twisted; costae long or short extending towards center but not quite to it, with intermediate striae more or less evident; central space linear to lanceolate, often obscure; with longitudinal central pseudoraphe and marginal, more or less elevated undulated keel produced into wing-like expansion including raphe on each side; pseudoraphes of the two valves parallel; raphe seen only with difficulty; distinct canal pores usually visible. Girdle view linear or wedge-shaped.
HABITAT: freshwater, brackish and marine.
S. fatuosa var. *recedens* (A. Schmidt) Cleve. Fig. 180 *(marine)*.
S. robusta Ehrenberg. Fig. 178. (freshwater).

Synedra Ehrenberg. (Pennate)
Cells single or in fan-like to clustered star-like colonies, seldom in short bands. Valves linear to very narrow lanceolate, sometimes with undulating margin, often wider in middle or at ends; apical axis greatly elongated, rod-like sometimes bent; surface usually with transapical rows of delicate punctae and narrower pseudoraphe or wider lanceolate hyaline central area often with scattered punctae. Girdle view lacking intercalary bands and septa, girdle band thus narrow-linear usually. Compare with solitary cells of **Fragilaria** in fresh waters, from which it may not be distinguishable.
HABITAT: freshwater, brackish and marine.
S. ulna (Nitzsch) Ehrenberg. Figs. 100, 103. *(freshwater)*.
S. undulata Bailey. Fig. 102. *(marine)*.

71

Tabellaria Ehrenberg. (Pennate)
Cells in straight filaments or zigzag chains or star-like clusters. Valves elongate with evident median inflation and slightly inflated poles; septa appear as short thick lines of varying length; with pseudoraphe on both valves. Girdle view rectangular, with intercalary bands; internal to wall and between girdles and intercalary bands are longitudinal septa extending almost to center of cell.
HABITAT: freshwater.
T. fenestrata (Lyngbye) Kützing. Figs. 166, 169.

Terpsinoe Ehrenberg. (Centric)
Cells solitary, in flat filaments or in zigzag chains. Valves elliptical or triangular with markedly undulating sides; with transverse septa within cells extending across the short axis. Girdle view with septa perpendicular to valve face extending inward to level of intercalary bands; internal margin of each septum thickened and bent at an angle to the other portion strongly suggesting a series of musical notes. Compare with the marine **Grammatophora.**
HABITAT: freshwater, but predominantly marine.
T. musica Ehrenberg. Fig. 29.

Tetracyclus Ralfs. (Pennate)
Cells filamentous or in zigzag chains. Girdle view rectangular, with longitudinal septa rarely extending more than 1/3 distance to middle of cell and are more or less curved at apices. Valves oval or inflated in middle; with a series of conspicuous internal costae (false septa) on valves which are usually transverse but may be oblique or interrupted in middle.
HABITAT: freshwater, especially cold mountain waters.
T. lacustris Ralfs. Fig. 165.

Thalassionema Grunow. (Pennate)
Cells in zigzag chains or star-shaped colonies by gelatinous cushions at cell angles. Valves linear to narrow lancet-shaped, with numerous tiny spines on margins at regular intervals; cells otherwise structureless. Girdle view linear, without septa or girdle bands.
HABITAT: marine plankton.
T. nitzschioides Grunow. Fig. 104.

Thalassiosira Cleve. (Centric)
Cells similar to **Coscinodiscus** usually drum- or disk-shaped, united in flexible chains by a single gelatinous thread or in formless gelatinous masses, seldom solitary. Valves with areolae or delicate radial rows of punctations (difficult to see); with marginal spinules usually distinct, sometimes with mucilage threads extruding which may be much longer than cell itself; face rounded or flat, in a few species depressed in center. Girdle view with one or more intercalary bands per valve.

HABITAT: freshwater (rare) and marine plankton, mainly cold and temperate seas.

T. aestivalis Gran. & Angst. Fig. 49. (marine).
T. decipiens (Grunow) Jorgensen. Fig. 51. (marine).
T. fluviatilis Hustedt. Fig. 48. (freshwater).
T. subtilis (Ostenfeld) Gran. Fig. 80. (marine).
T. nordenskioldii Cleve. Fig. 50.

Thalassiothrix Cleve & Grunow. (Pennate)
Cells solitary, rod-shaped, straight or slightly bent, in bunches or star-like groups or in zigzag chains, united by gelatinous cushions at ends. Valves narrow linear, borders often beset with spines; surface with short marginal striae or structureless. Girdle view linear, narrow. **T. longissima** with cells up to 4mm. long and 3-6 μm wide is the longest diatom known.
T. frauenfeldii Grunow. Figs. 97, 99.
T. longissima Cleve and Grunow. Fig. 101.

Triceratium Ehrenberg. (Centric)
Cells solitary, in filaments or zigzag chains. Valves triangular, center convex, lacking spines; with three terminal processes robust, elevated, finely punctate up to ends; margins straight or somewhat convex; walls sculpturing with coarse hexagonal cells allowing fine puncta of inner surface to be seen; partitions of cells with small spines. Girdle face much longer than wide, lacking costae; connecting zone delicately striate lengthwise with punctae in groups like "5-spot" dice.
HABITAT: marine plankton.
T. favus Ehrenberg. Fig. 32.

List of Synonyms

Ceratoneis Ehrenberg = **Hannaea** (Ehrenberg) Patrick.
Entomoneis Ehrenberg = **Amphiprora** (Ehrenberg) Cleve.
Eucocconeis flexella (Kützing) Hust. = **Achnanthes flexella** (Kützing) Brun.
Tropodoneis Cleve = **Plagiotropis** Pfitzer.

Taxonomic References

1. Anonymous. 1966. A Guide to the Common Diatoms at Water Pollution Surveillance System Stations. U.S.D.I., Federal Water Pollution Control Adm., Water Pollution Surveillance. 101pp, illus.
2. Bourrelly, P. 1968. Les Algues d'eau douce. Vol. 2. Les Algues Jaunes et Brunes. Boubee & Cie, Paris. 438 pp., 114 pls.
3. Boyer, C. S. 1916. The Diatomaceae of Philadelphia and Vicinity. J. B. Lippincott Co., Philadelphia. 143 pp., 40 pls. (Reprint, University Microfilms, Ann Arbor).
4. Boyer. 1927. Synopsis of the North American Diatomaceae. Part 1, 2. Suppl: 1-228; 229-583. Proc. Acad. Nat. Sci. Phila. 78, 79. (Reprint, University Microfilms, Ann Arbor).
5. Brunnel, J. 1962. Le Phytoplancton de la Baie des Challeurs. Univ. Montreal Press. 365 pp., illus.
6. Cleve, P. T. 1894, 1895. Synopsis of the Naviculoid diatoms. I-II. Kongliga Svenska Vetenskaps-Akademiens Handlingar, Ny Foljd, 26(2): 1-194; 27(3): 1-219. Illus.
7. Collier, A. and A. Murphy. 1962. Very Small Diatoms: Preliminary Notes and Description of Chaetoceros Galvestonensis. Science 136: 780-781. Fig. 1.
8. Cupp, Easter. 1943. Marine Plankton Diatoms of the West Coast of North America. Bull. Scripps. Inst. Oceanogr. 5: 1-238. Illus.
9. Curl, H., Jr. 1959. The Phytoplankton of Apalachee Bay and the Northeastern Gulf of Mexico. Inst. Marine Science 6: 277-320. 125 figs.
10. Elmore, C. J. 1922. The Diatoms (Bacillariodae) of Nebraska. Univ. Nebraska Studies 21: 22-214. 23 pls.
11. Engler, A. and K. Prantl. 1928. Die Natürlichen Pflanzenfamilien. W. Engelman, Leipzig. 345 pp.
12. Freese, L. R. 1952. Marine Diatoms of the Rockport, Texas, Bay Area. Texas J. of Sci. 4(3): 331-386. Illus.
13. Gleave, H. H. 1972. *Hydrosira triquetra*, a Diatom New to Europe Waters. Microscopy 32: 208.
14. Gran, H. H. 1905. Diatomeen. In Brandt, K. and C. Apstein, eds., Nordische Plankton. Bd. 19, p. 1-146. Illus.
15. Gran, H. H. and E. C. Angst. 1931. Plankton Diatoms of Puget Sound. Puget Sound Biological Station Publ. 7: 417-519. 95 figs.
16. Hanna, G Dallas. 1959. Index to Atlas der Diatomaceen-Kunde von Adolf Schmidt. Verlag von J. Cramer. xvi + 208 pp.
17. Huber-Pestalozzi, G. 1942. Die Binnengewässer. Das Phytoplankton des Süsswassers. 2 Teil. 2 Hälfte. Diatomeen. Stuttgart. 549 pp., 645 figs.
18. Hustedt, F. 1927-1966. Die Kieselalgen Deutschlands, Österreichs und der Schweiz. In L. Rabenhorst's Kryptogamen-Flora. Vol. 7, Part 1 (920 p.), Part 2 (845 pp.), Part 3 (816 pp.). Illus. (Reprint, Johnson Reprints Inc., New York).

19. Hustedt, F. 1930. Bacillariophyta (Diatomeae), In A. Pascher,ed., Die Süsswasser-Flora Mitteleuropas. 2d ed. viii + 466 pp., 875 figs. (Reprint, Univ. Microfilms, Ann Arbor).

20. Hustedt, F. 1955. Marine Littoral Diatoms of Beaufort, North Carolina. Duke Univ. Press, Durham, NC.

21. Mills, F. W. 1933-1935. An Index to the Genera and Species of the Diatomaceae and their Synonyms; p.1444-1726 (1935).

22. Patrick, R. and C. W. Reimer. 1966; 1975. The Diatoms of the United States. Vol. 1; 2 (Part 1). Monogr. Acad. Nat. Sci. Philadelphia No. 13. 688 pp., 64 pls.; 213 pp., 28 pls.

23. Schmidt, A. 1874-1959. Atlas der Diatomaceenkunde. R. Reisland, Leipzig. Pl. 1-472.

24. Smith, G. M. 1950. The Fresh-water Algae of the United States. 2d ed. McGraw-Hill, New York. 719 pp., 559 figs.

25. Tiffany, L. H. and M. E. Britton. 1952. The Algae of Illinois. Univ. Chicago Press.

26. van Heurck, H. 1896. A Treatise on the Diatomaceae. Transl. by W. E. Baxter. (Reprint 1962, Wheldon and Wesley, Ltd., London. xx + 559 pp., 35 pls., 291 text figs.

27. van Landingham, S. L. 1967-1979. Catalog of the Fossil and Recent Genera and Species of Diatoms and their Synonyms Vols. 1-8. 4654 pp. J. Cramer, Lehre, Germany.

28. Vinyard, W. C. 1974. Key to the Genera of Diatoms of the Inland Waters of Temperate North America. Mad River Press, Eureka, CA. 19 pp., illus.

29. Vinyard, W.C. 1975. A Key to the Genera of Marine Planktonic Diatoms of the Pacific Coast of North America. Mad River Press, Eureka, CA. 26 pp., illus.

DERIVATIONS
OF GENERIC NAMES

Centric Diatoms

Actinocyclus   Gr. *actino*, a ray + *cyclus*, circle.
Actinoptychus   Gr. *actino*, a ray + *ptych*, fold.
Asterolampra   Gr. *astero*, a star + *lampr*, brilliant, beautiful.
Asteromphalus   Gr. *astero*, a star + *omphal*, the navel.
Attheya   (A memorial name?).
Aulacodiscus   Gr. *aulaco*, a furrow + *discus*, disc.
Auliscus   Gr. *aul*, a pipe + *iscus*, dimunitive.
Bacteriastrum   Gr. *bacter*, a rod + *aster*, a star.
Bacteriosira   Gr. *bacter*, a rod + *seir*, a chain.
Bellarochia   (A memorial name).
Biddulphia   (A memorial name).
Ceratulina   Gr. *cerat*, horn + *uli*, twisted.
Chaetoceros   Gr. *chaeto*, a bristle + *cerat*, horn.
Climacodium   Gr. *climac*, a ladder + *codia*, the head.
Corethron   Gr. *corethrum*, a broom.
Coscinodiscus   Gr. *coscin*, a seive + *discus*, disc.
Coscinosira   Gr. *coscin*, a seive + *seir*, a chain.
Cyclotella   Gr. *cyclo*, a circle + L. *ella*, diminutive.
Dactyliosolen   Gr. *dactyl*, finger or toe + *solen*, a pipe.
Detonula   (A memorial name?).
Ditylum   Gr. *di*, two + *tyl*, a knob.
Eucampia   Gr. *eu*, well + *camp*, bending.
Eupodiscus   Gr. *eu*, good + *pod*, foot + *discus*, disc.
Guinardia   (A memorial name).
Hemiaulus   Gr. *hemi*, one-half + *aulus*, a pipe.
Hemidiscus   Gr. *hemi*, one-half + *discus*, a disc.
Hyalodiscus   Gr. *hyalo*, shining, transparent + *discus*, a disc.
Hydrosira   Gr. *hydro*, water + *seira*, band or chain.
Isthmia   Gr. *isthm*, a narrow passage.
Lauderia   (A memorial name).
Leptocylindrus   Gr. *lept*, slender + *cylind*, a cylinder.
Lithodesmium   Gr. *litho*, a stone + *desm*, a band.
Melosira   Gr. *melo*, a gruit + *seir*, a chain.
Porosira   Latin. *por*, a pore + Gr. *seir*, a chain.
Pseudaluliscus   Gr. *pseud*, deceptive + **Auliscus** (generic name).
Rhizosolenia   Gr. *rhizo*, root + *solen*, a pipe.
Schroederella   (A memorial to Schroder) + L. *ella*, diminutive.
Skeletonema   Gr. *skeleto*, skeleton + *nema*, a thread.
Stephanodiscus   Gr. *stephano*, a crown + G. *discus*, a disc.
Stephanopyxis   Gr. *stephano*, a crown + *pyxis*, a box.
Streptotheca   Gr. *strepto*, twisted + *theca*, box.

77

Terpsinoe Gr. *terpsinoos*, delight, heart gladening.
Thalassiosira Gr. *thalass*, the sea + *seir*, a chain.
Triceratium Latin. *tri*, three + *cerat*, horn.

Pennate Diatoms

Achnanthes Gr. *achn*, excellence + *anth*, flower.
Actinella Gr. *actin*, a ray or beam + Latin. *ella*, diminutive.
Amphicampa Gr. *amphi*, on both sides + *campo*, a bending.
Amphipleura Gr. *amphi*, on both sides + *pleura*, a rib.
Amphiprora Gr. *amphi*, on both sides + *prora*, prow of a ship.
Amphora Gr. *amphora*, a two-eared pitcher, flask.
Anomoeoneis Gr. *anomoe*, dissimiliar + *neis*, feeble.
Asterionella Gr. *aster*, a star + Latin. *ella*, diminutive.
Brebissonia (A memorial name).
Caloneis Gr. *calo*, beautiful + *neis*, feeble.
Campylodiscus Gr. *camp*, a bending + *discus*, a disc.
Campylosira Gr. *camp*, a bending + *seira*, a chain.
Capartogramma (?)
Centronella Gr. *centro*, center + Latin. *ella*, diminutive.
Climacosphenia Gr. *climac*, a ladder + *sphen*, a wedge.
Cocconeis Gr. *cocco*, a berry + *neis*, feeble.
Cylindrotheca Gr. *cylindro*, a cylinder + *theca*, box.
Cymatopleura Gr. *cym*, a wave + *pleura*, the side.
Cymbella Gr. *cymb*, a cup, boat + Latin. *ella*, diminutive.
Denticula Latin. *dent*, tooth + *cula*, little.
Diatoma Gr. *di*, through + *tom*, cut.
Diatomella (***Diatoma***, a generic name) + Latin. *ella*, diminutive.
Didymosphenia Gr. *didymo*, double + *sphen*, a wedge.
Diploneis Gr. *diplo*, double + *neis*, feeble.
Epithemia Gr. *epithem*, a cover, lid.
Eunotia Gr. *eu*, true, good or well + (?) *not*, back.
Fragilaria Latin. *fragil*, fragile + *aria*, connected.
Frickia (A memorial name).
Frustulia Latin. *frustul*, a little piece.
Gomphoneis Gr. *gompho*, wedge-shaped + *neis*, feeble.
Gomphonema Gr. *gompho*, wedge-shaped + *nema*, a thread.
Gomphonitzschia Gr. *gompho*, wedge-shaped + **Nitzschia**, a generic name; or ***Gomphonema***, a generic name + **Nitzschia**, a generic name.
Grammatophora Gr. *grammat*, linear, linear lined + *phora*, to bear.
Gyrosigma Latin. *gyro*, turning + *sigma*, S-shaped.
Hannaea (A memorial name).
Hantzschia (A memorial name).
Licmophora Latin. *lic*, thread + *phora*, to bear.
Mastogloia Gr. *masto*, nipple + *gloi*, gelatinous, glue.
Meridion Gr. *merid*, a part + *idio*, distinct.
Navicula Latin. *navicula*, a little boat.

Neidium Gr. *neid,* feeble + *idium,* diminutive.
Nitzschia (A memorial name).
Oestrupia (A memorial name).
Opephora Gr. *ope,* opening + *phora,* to bear.
Peronia Gr. *peron,* the fibula.
Pinnularia Latin. *pinnula,* feather.
Plagiogramma Gr. *plagio,* oblique, the sides + *gramma,* a line, linear
lined.
Plagiotropis Gr. *plagio,* oblique, the sides + *trophia,* a keel.
Pleurosigma Gr. *pleur,* a rib + *sigma,* S-shaped.
Pseudoeunotia Gr. *pseudo,* deceptive + **Eunotia,** a generic name.
Rhabdonema Gr. *rhabdo,* a rod + *nema,* thread.
Rhoicosphenia Gr. *rhoicos,* crooked + *sphen,* wedge.
Rhopalodia Gr. *rophal,* a club + *ode,* form.
Scoliopleura Gr. *scolio,* curved + *pleura,* a rib.
Semiorbis Latin. *semi,* half + *orbi,* circle.
Stauroneis Gr. *stauro,* a cross + *neis,* feeble.
Striatella Latin. *striat,* furrow, streak + *ella,* diminutive.
Surirella (?) + Latin. *ella,* diminutive.
Synedra Gr. *syn,* together + *edra,* dwelling, sedentary.
Tabellaria Latin. *tabell,* a little tablet + *aria,* connected.
Tetracyclus Gr. *tetr,* four + *cycle,* a circle.
Thalassionema Gr. *thalass,* the sea + *nema,* thread.
Thalassiothrix Gr. *thalass,* the sea + *thrix,* hair.

Marine Diatoms
By Ernst Haeckel, 1904. (Courtesy of Dover Publications, *Artforms in Nature*, 1974.)

GLOSSARY
OF TAXONOMIC TERMS

ADJOINED. In contact with each other.
AREOLAE. (= ALVEOLAE). Polygonal or rounded pores in valve wall, often honey-comb-like.
ALVEOLAE. (= AREOLAE).
AMORPHOUS. Lacking a definable shape.
APICAL AXIS. Longitudinal axis of a valve. Raphe or pseudoraphe lies in this axis or is eccentric to it.
APICAL PLANE. Axial plane perpendicular to the transapical axis.
APICAL VIEW. (= BROAD GIRDLE VIEW). View with transapical axis parallel to the axis of the viewer.
ARCUATE. Arched or bow-shaped.
AXIAL AREA. The clear area between raphe and ends of transverse striae.
BROAD GIRDLE VIEW. (See **APICAL VIEW**).
CANAL RAPHE. A raphe lying in a groove or channel, usually located in a more or less marked crest or keell.
CAPITATE. Swollen at the apex.
CATENATE. A series of cells placed lend to end in a bead-like series or chain.
CENTRAL AREA. The clear area in the center of the valve around the central nodule so that they appear as one.
CENTRAL NODULE. A thickened area between the two central pores of the raphe. See **CENTRAL AREA**.
CLAVATE. Club-shaped.
COLONIAL. A group of cells held together by a more or less conspicuous gelatinous secretion, the whole of definite shape, or amorphous.
CONNECTING BANDS. The ring-shaped inner part (rim) which, with the mantle, constitutes a valve. Connecting bands appear as lines in side view or **GIRDLE VIEW**. See **GIRDLE**.
COPULAE. (= INTERCALARY BANDS).
COSTAE. Ribs or thickenings appearing as double lines in the wall (cf. **STRIAE**).
CUNEATE. Wedge-shaped.
CYMBAEFORM. Cymbal-form.
DENTATE. Toothed, the teeth if spinelike, very short.
DISCOID. Like a disc or shortened cylinder.
ELLIPTICAL. Shape with sides forming ellipses, or plane curves.
EPITHECA. (= EPIVALVE).
EPIVALVE (= EPITHECA). The upper, and therefore older, half of a frustule which fits closely over the **HYPOVALVE**.
FASCICLE. A bundle or cluster.

FILAMENT. A row of cells joined end to end, or side by side, either adjoined or held together in line by gelatinous threads.

FRUSTULE. The cell wall (shell) of a diatom composed of two **VALVES** joined by a **CONNECTING BAND** known as a **GIRDLE.**

GIRDLE. (See **CONNECTING BANDS**). Bands of silica attached to each valve mantle, one girdle overlapping the other.

GIRDLE VIEW. Side view, with the overlapping halves **(VALVES)** of the **FRUSTULE** apparent, the **GIRDLE** uppermost in optical view.

GREGARIOUS. Congregated, but not held together as by gelatinous secretions.

HORN. A much elongated process which is not noticeabley tapered. (cf. **SPINE**).

HYPOTHECA. (= HYPOVALVE).

HYPOVALVE (= HYPOTHECA). The lower (and younger) half of the frustule within the **EPITHECA.**

INTERCALARY. Inserted between the usual elements.

INTERCALARY BANDS. Bands of silica often occuring between the **VALVE MANTLE** and the **GIRDLE.** These are variable in number and width and sometimes extend into the valve to form a **SEPTUM.**

KEEL. A flange or projection of the **VALVE** surface, as a keel of a boat, usually more or less eccentric to the **APICAL AXIS.** In it is enclosed the **CANAL RAPHE** which is characteristic of certain genera.

KEEL PUNCTAE. Pores, or membranes appearing as pores, in the plate lying below the **CANAL RAPHE.** These "carinal dots" (carinal = canal) are quite conspicuous and characterize a few genera.

LANCEOLATE. Lance-shaped: long and narrow with subparallel margins and tapered at the apex.

LINEAR. Long and narrow with sides parallel.

LONGITUDINAL. Along the long axis (cf.**TRANSVERSE**).

LONGITUDINDAL AREA. (= AXIAL AREA).

LONGITUDINAL AXIS. (= APICAL AXIS).

LUNATE. Crescent-shaped.

MAMILLATE. With a nipple-like protuberance.

MANTLE (= VALVE MANTLE). The outermost part of the valve that is apparent in girdle view, but excluding the connecting band; the broad surface as seen in valve view.

NARROW GIRDLE VIEW. (= TRANSAPICAL VIEW).

NAVICULAR. Boat-like; boat-shaped.

NODULE. A small knob; internal wall thickening located centrally or at the the poles; thus either **CENTRAL NODULES** or **POLAR NODULES,** between which lie the raphe.

OB—. Used as a prefix and meaning inversed.

OBLANCEOLATE. Lanceolate, but broader toward one pole.

OBLIQUE. Slanting or inclined; not perpendicular.

OVAL. Elongate and rounded with curvature the same at both poles.

POLAR NODULE. An enlarged, usually thickened, area of the wall in which the raphe terminates, forming an external and an internal fissure.

PERVALVAR AXIS. A line connecting the middle point of the two valves.

PROCESS. Any structure proceeding from, or projecting; any extension of a cell such as a spine, or horn.

PSUEDORAPHE. A clear axial line devoid of wall markings or of a raphe; a longitudinal clear space laterally separating the 2 vertical series of transverse striae, either median in position, or eccentric.

PUNCTA. PUNCTAE. Minute pores or dots; valve markings usually in rows (cf. **STRIAE**).

QUADRATE. Square or approximately so.

RAPHE. An axial groove-like slit in the main axis of the valve. Characteristic only of motile pennate genera.

RHOMBIC. In the form of a rhombus, which is a parallelogram having its angles oblique.

SEPTA. Incomplete partitions running parallel with the valves, and which result from internal extensions of the intercalary bands. They may extend completely across the valve, or may be only developed at the margin.

SESSILE. Attached to the substrate by gelatinous secretions.

SIGMOID. "S"-shaped (more or less), the apices curving in opposite directions.

SPINE. An elongate process tapering to a blunt or sharp tip.

STAUROS (Gr. *staur*, cross). A central nodule that extends almost to the margins of the valve and which is thickened and expanded, and which with a clear axial area appears as a cross.

STRIAE. Delicate, long, line-like markings usually occuring in parallel rows; lines of punctae so crowded as to appear as a solid line.

SETA. A slender, bristle-like organ or part; a long thin **SPINE.**

SUB—. A prefix denoting a lesser degree of the term which it is combined with.

SUBORBICULAR. Nearly, but not quite, circular or spherical.

TERMINAL NODULE. (= POLAR NODULE).

TRANSAPICAL AXIS. The transverse axis of the valve.

TRANSAPICAL PLANE. An axial plane perpendicular to the **APICAL AXIS.**

TRANSAPICAL VIEW. (= NARROW GIRDLE VIEW) View with apical axis turned toward observer.

TRANSVERSE. Across the short dimension.

TRANSVERSE AXIS. (= TRANSAPICAL AXIS). The axis of the valve that connects the two margins of the valve and is perpendicular to the apical axis.

TRUNCATE. Having the ends square or even.

TUMID. Swollen.

UNDULATE. Wavy in outline.

VALVE. One of two overlapping halves of a frustule composed of a flattened or undulate surface and a mantle which is perpendicular to it. (See **EPIVALVE** and **HYPOVALVE).**

VALVAR PLANE. An axial plane perpendicular to the pervalvar axis.

VALVE MANTLE. The portion of the valve that is apparent in girdle view (See **MANTLE**).

VALVE VIEW. View in pennate diatoms from the top or bottom so that the broader, flatter surface of the valve is seen, the valve side uppermost; the view one sees looking upon the surface of the valve. In centric forms the more or less circular (or angular) end view.

WING. A thin projection of the valve surface, much better developed than a keel, often arising near the apical axis of the valve but becoming most apparent at the junction of the valve with the valve mantle, where the surface of the valve may be distinctly elevated. The canal raphe may be enclosed in the wing.

EXPLANATION OF FIGURES

(Source of figures indicated by numbers in parentheses referring to listing of taxonomic references)

Figures 1-12

1. ***Coscinodiscus lacustris.*** Valve view. (28)
2. ***C. lineatus.*** Valve view. (8)
3. ***C. granii.*** Girdle view. (8)
4. ***C. radiatus.*** Detail of wall sculpture. (8)
5. ***Actinoptychus undulaltus.*** a, valve view; b, girdle view. (14)
6. ***Actinocyclus ehrenbergii.*** Valve view. (19)
7. ***Stephanodiscus niagrae.*** a, valve view; b, girdle view. (26)
8. ***Cyclotella meneghinii.*** a, valve view; b, girdle view. (1)
9. ***Cyclotella antiqua.*** Valve view. (28)
10. ***Hyalodiscus subtilis.*** Valve view. (19)
11. ***Cyclotella bodanica.*** Girdle view. (1)
12. ***Pseudauliscus radiatus.*** Valve view. (9)

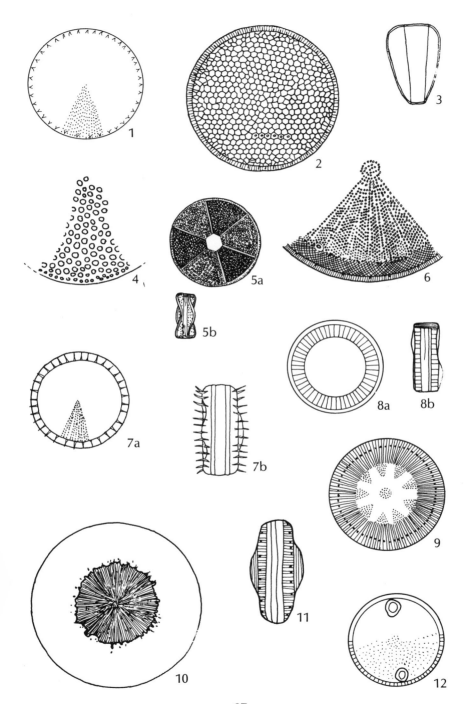

Figures 13-20

13. Hemidiscus hardmanianus. Oblique view of cell. (9)
14. H. cuneiforme var. **ventricosa.** a, valve view; b, c, oblique views of cell. (8)
15. Auliscus sculptus. a, valve view; b, girdle view. (26)
16. Eupodiscus argus. Valve sculpture. (26)
17. E. argus. Girdle view. (26)
18. Asteromphalus heptactis. Valve view. (8)
19. Aulacodiscus kittoni. Valve view, detail drawn from photomicrograph. (8)
20. Asterolalmpra marylandica. Valve view. (8)

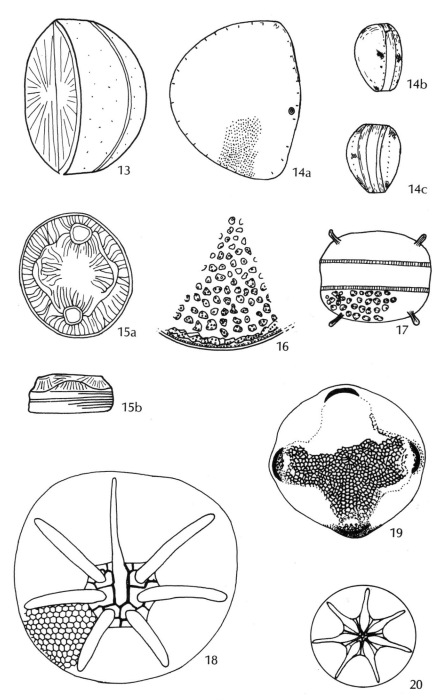

Figures 21-33

21. *Biddulphia aurita.* Girdle view, individual from central Mexico. (8)

22. *B. aurita.* Girdle view, individual from southern California. (8)

23. *B. laevis.* a, valve view; b, girdle view. (8)

24. *B. aurita.* Girdle view. (8)

25. *B. laevis.* Valve view. (2)

26. *B. longicruris* var.*hyalina.* Two cells of a filament in girdle view.(8)

27. *B. longicruris.* Narrow girdle view. (8)

28. *B. longicruris.* Broad girdle view. (8)

29. *Terpsinoe musica.* a, valve view; b, girdle view showing septa resembling musical notes. (2)

30. *Arachnodiscus ehrenbergii.* Valve view, detail of sculpture. (15)

31. *Planktoniella sol.* Valve view. (15)

32. *Triceratium favus.* a, valve view; b, girdle view. (9)

33. *Isthmia nervosa.* Girdle view, showing zigzag attachments to other cells. (8)

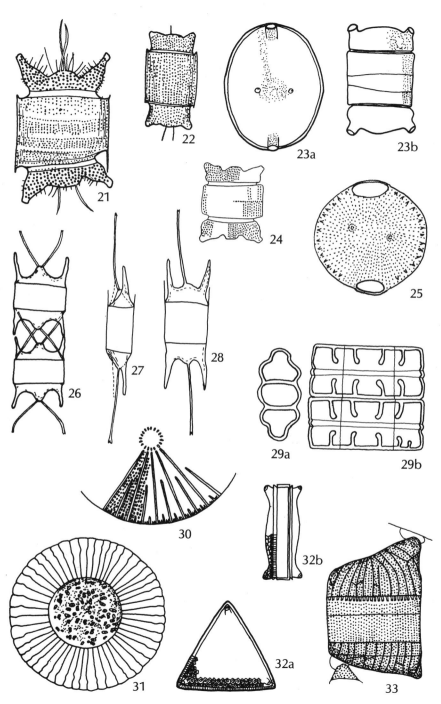

Figures 34-47

*34. **Melosira varians.*** Part of filament, cells in girdle view. (28)
*35. **M. moniliformis.*** Part of filament. (15)
*36. **M. granulata.*** Part of filament. (17)
*37. **M binderana.*** Part of filament. (1)
*38. **M. sulcata.*** Part of filament. (8)
*39. **Guinardia flaccida.*** Part of a cell with girdle bands. (8)
*40. **Leptocylindrus danicus.*** Part of a filament. (8)
*41. **Bacterosira fragilis.*** Part of a filament, cells with intercalary bands; drawn from photomicrograph. (5)
*42. **Detonula confervacea.*** Part of a filament, cells with intercalary bands; drawn from photomicrograph. (5)
*43. **Dactyliosolen antarcticus.*** Part of a filament, cells with intercalary bands. (8)
*44. **Bellarochia malleus.*** Part of a filament, cells in girdle view. (26)
*45. **Bellarochia malleus.*** Part of a filament, cells in girdle view. (9)
*46. **Lithodesmium undulatum.*** a, cell in oblique view showing valve; b, part of a filament with cells in girdle view. (8)
*47. **Streptotheca thamensis.*** Part of a filament, cells in girdle view. (8)

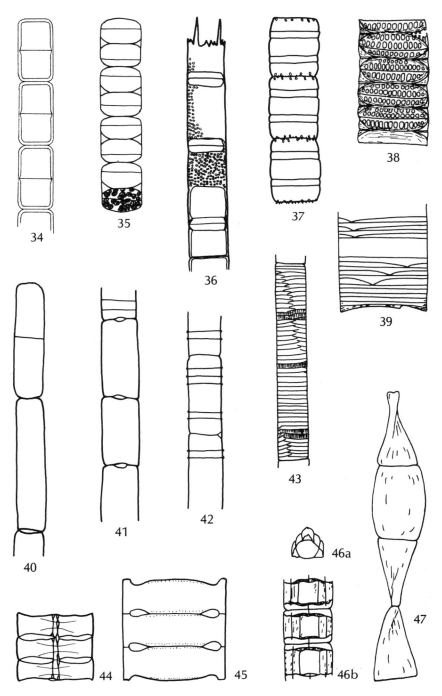

34 35 36 37 38 39 40 41 42 43 44 45 46a 46b 47

93

Figures 48-61

48. *Thalassiosira fluviatilis.* a, valve view; b, girdle view. (2)

49. *T. aestivalis.* Part of a filament, cells in girdle view. (8)

50. *T. nordenskioldii.* Part of a filament, cells in girdle view. (8)

51. *T. decipiens.* Three cells in oblique, one in girdle view. (8)

52. *Coscinosira polychorda.* Part of a filament, cells in girdle view. (8)

53. *Schroederella delicatula.* Part of a filament, cells in girdle view with intercalary bands. (8)

54. *Lauderia borealis.* Cell in girdle view with intercalary bands. (8)

55. *Ditylum brightwellii.* Cell in girdle view. (8)

56. *D. brightwellii.* a, girdle view; b, valve view. (26)

57. *Porosira glacialis.* Part of a filament, drawn from a photomicrograph. (5)

58. *Ceratulina bergonii.* Part of a filament with cells in girdle view. (8)

59. *Skeletonema costatum.* Parts of filaments with cells in girdle view: a, cells of small diameter; b, greater diameter. (8)

60. *Stephanopyxis palmeriana.* Part of a filament with cells in girdle view. (8)

61. *S. turris.* Detail of wall sculpture sample and connecting tubules. (8)

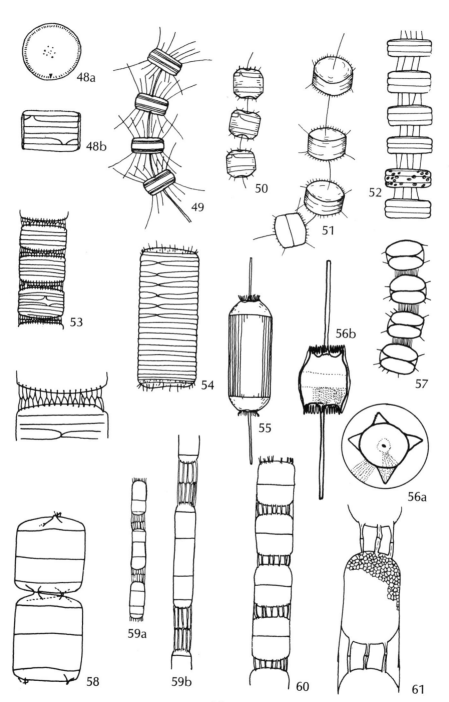

48a

48b

49

50

51

52

53

54

55

56b

57

56a

58

59a

59b

60

61

95

Figures 62-70

62. *Chaetoceros radicans.* Valve view. (8)

63. *C. elmorei.* a, valve view; b, part of filament with cells in girdle view. (17)

64. *C. didymus.* Part of a filament with cells in girdle view. (8)

65. *C. concavicornis.* Part of a filament with cells in girdle view. (8)

66. *C. gracilis.* Girdle view. (8)

67. *Bacteriastrum delicatulum.* Valve view. (8)

68. *Chaetoceros galvestonensis.* Girdle view. (7)

69. *Bacteriastrum delicatulum.* Part of a filament with cells in girdle view. (8)

70. *Corethron hystrix.* Girdle view. (8)

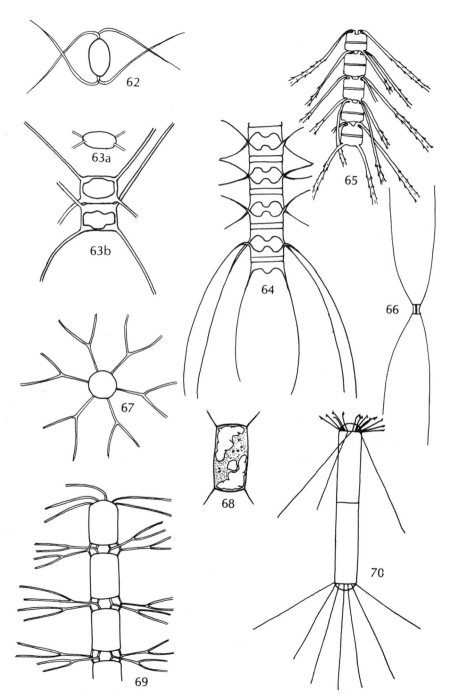

62

63a

63b

64

65

66

67

68

69

70

97

Figures 71-80

71. *Rhizosolenia eriensis.* Girdle view with intercalary bands. (19)
72. *R. setigera.* Girdle view. (15)
73. *R. longiseta.* Girdle view. (19)
74. *R. alata* fa. *curvirostris.* Girdle view. (8)
75. *R. robusta.* Broad girdle view. (8)
76. *Attheya decora.* Girdle view. (26)
77. *Rhizosolenia stolterfothii.* a, part of a filament; b, cell in girdle view with intercalary bands. (8)
78. *Attheya zachariasi.* Girdle view. (19)
79. *Rhizosolenia styliformis.* a, ventral view of apart of a cell; b, side view of same cell. (8)
80. *Thalassiosira subtilis.* Amorphous colony. (8)

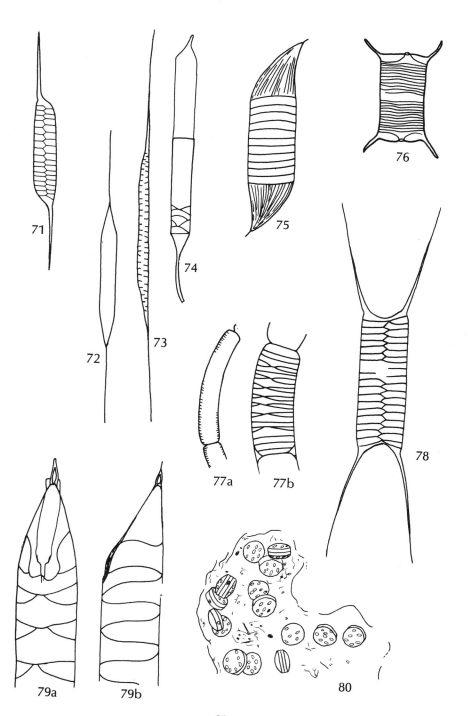

71

72

73

74

75

76

77a

77b

78

79a

79b

80

99

Figures 81-93

81. ***Eucampia zoodiacus.*** *a,* valve view; *b,* part of a filament with cells in girdle view.

82. ***Hemiaulus membranaceous.*** Part of a filament with cells in girdle view. (9)

83. ***H. hauckii.*** Part of a filament with cells in girdle view. (8)

84. ***Climacodium frauenfeldianum.*** Part of a filament with cells in girdle view. (8)

85. ***Hydrosera triquetra.*** Valve view with sample of wall sculpture. (13)

86. ***Centronella reichelti.*** Valve view. (19)

87. ***Fragilaria crotonensis.*** Part of a filament with cells in girdle view. (8)

88. ***F. islandica.*** Part of a filament with cells in girdle view. (14)

89. ***Pseudoeunotia doliolus.*** Part of a filament, inner cells in girdle view, end cells in valve view. (8)

90. ***Achnanthes inflata.*** *a,* valve view; *b,* girdle view. (2)

91. ***Campylosira cymbelliformis.*** Part of a filament with cells in girdle view. (8)

92. ***Plagiogramma vanheurckii.*** Part of a filament with cells in girdle view. (8)

93. ***Achnanthes longipes.*** Part of a filament with cells in girdle view. (8)

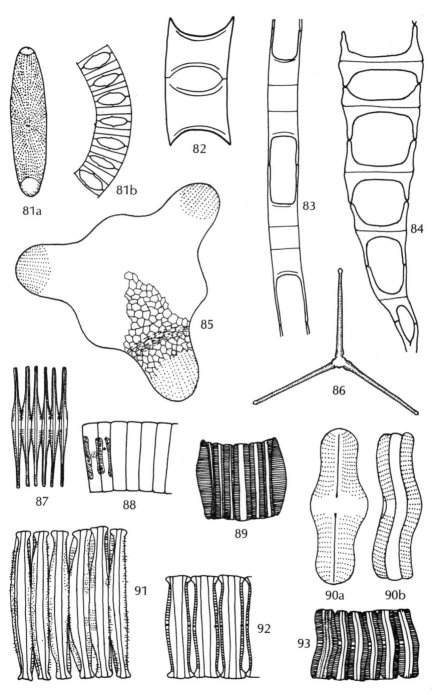

81a 81b 82 83 84 85 86 87 88 89 90a 90b 91 92 93

101

Figures 94-104

94. Asterionella formosa. Colony with cells in girdle view. (28)
95. A. japponica. a, part of a colony with cells in girdle view; b, two cells in girdle view. (8)
96. A. japponica. Cells in girdle view enlarged. (8)
97. Thalassiothrix frauenfeldii. Detail of part of two cells in girdle view. (8)
98. Asterionella kariana. Part of a colony with cells in girdle view. (8)
99. Thalassiothrix frauenfeldii. Colony with cells in girdle view. (8)
100. Synedra ulna. Colony. (28)
101. Thalassiothrix longissimum. Cell outline. (8)
102. Synedra undulata. a, valve view. b, girdle view. (8)
103. Synedra ulna. Girdle view. (28)
104. Thalassionema nitzschioides. a, valve view; b, zigzag chain of recently divided cells; c, zigzag chain with cells in girdle view. (8)

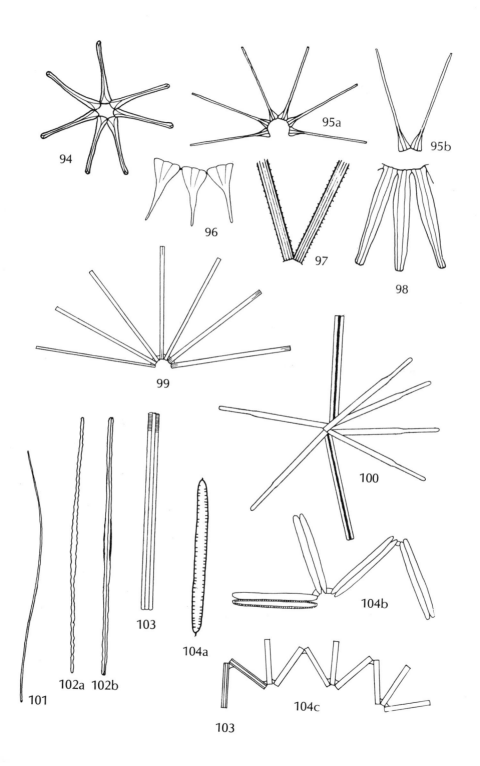

94

95a

95b

96

97

98

99

100

101

102a 102b

103

104a

104b

104c

103

Figures 105-115

105. Amphora ovalis. a, valve view; b, girdle view with both raphes visible. (28)

106. Hannaea arcus. Valve view. (2)

107. Epithemia argus. a, valve view (28); b, girdle view (24)

108. Semiorbis hemicyclus. Valve view. (2)

109. Eunotia robusta. Valve view. (2)

110. Amphicampa eruca. Valve view. (2)

111. Rhabdonema adriaticum. Girdle view. (9)

112. Striatella unipunctata. Girdle view. (8)

113. Cymbella aspera. Valve view. 28)

114. Rhopalodia gibba. a, valve view (3); b, girdle view. (28)

115. Rhoicosphenia curvata. a, valve view with raphe; b, valve view with pseudoraphe; c, girdle view. (2)

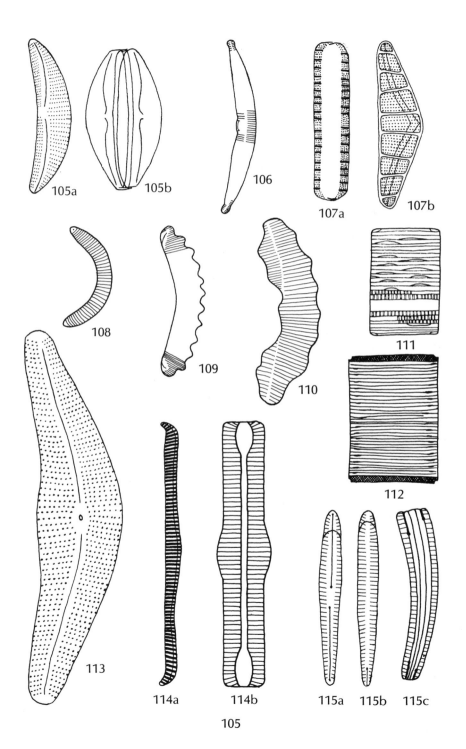

105a 105b 106 107a 107b

108 109 110 111

113 112

114a 114b 115a 115b 115c

105

Figures 116-129

116. *Climacosphenia moniligera.* a, valve view; b, girdle view. (8)
117. *Licmophora abbreviata.* Girdle view of cells on gelatinous stalks. (44)
118. *Meridion circulare.* Part of a filament, cells in girdle view. (28)
119. *Peronia erinacea.* a, valve view with pseudoraphe; b, girdle view; c, valve view with raphes. (19)
120. *Gomphonema acuminatum.* Valve view. (1)
121. *Actinella punctata.* a, valve view with pseudoraphe; b, *girdle view.*
122. *Opephora martyi.* a, valve view; b, girdle view. (19)
123. *Licmophora longipes.* Girdle view. (8)
124. *Gomphonema olivaceum.* Girdle view. (1)
125. *G. turris.* Valve view. (1)
126. *Didymosphenia geminata.* Valve view with details of raphe and central area (transverse rows of bead-like punctae omitted). (22)
127. *Gomphoneis herculeana.* Valve view. (2)
128. *Gomphonema constricta.* a, valve view; b, girdle view. (28)
129. *Gomphonema geminatum.* Valve view. (1)

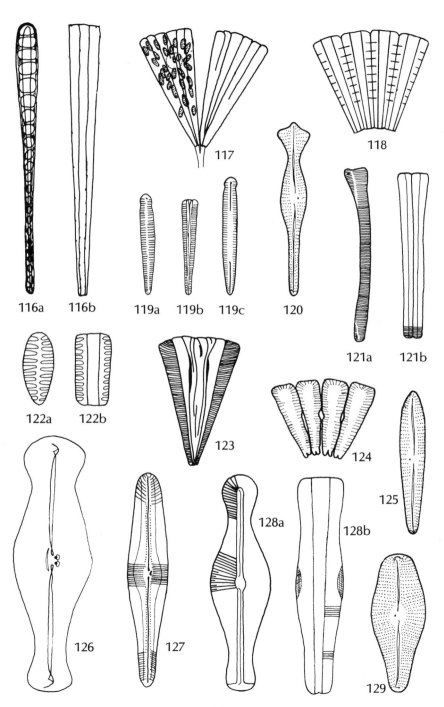

116a 116b 119a 119b 119c 120 117 118 121a 121b

122a 122b 123 124 125 126 127 128a 128b 129

Figures 130-138

130. Diploneis finnica. Valve view. (28)
131. Cocconeis placentula. Raphe-bearing valve. (28)
132. Gyrosigma spenceri. a, valve view outline; b, valve sculpture detail. (8)
133. Achnanthes flexella. Valve view. (2)
134. Scoliopleura peisonis. Valve view. (6)
135. Pleurosigma hamulifera. Valve view with details of striae pattern. (8)
136. Plagiotropis lepidoptera var **proboscidea.** Girdle view. (8)
137. P. lepidoptera. a, valve view of cell in one position; b, valve view of cell in different position. (1)
138. Pleurosigma elongatum. Valve view outline. (8)

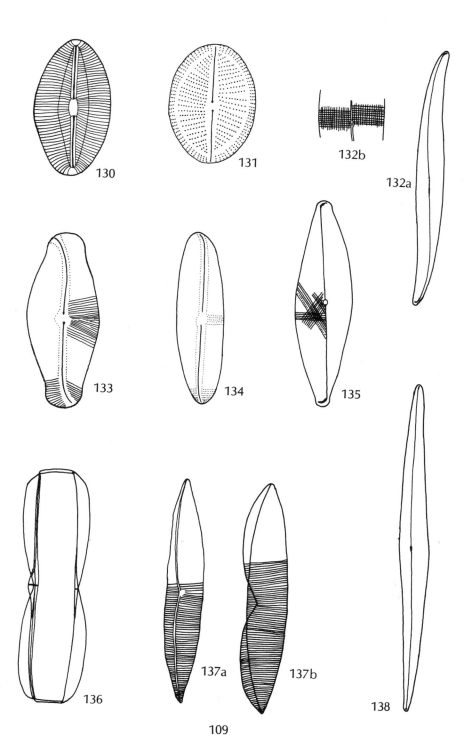

Figures 139-147

139. Cylindrotheca gracilis. Cell with spiral raphes. (2)
140. Gomphonitzschia ungeri. a, valve view; b, girdle view. (2)
141. Nitzschia paradoxa. Colony with cells in girdle view. (8)
142. Hantzschia amphioxis. Valve view. (2)
143. Nitzschia sigmoidea. a, valve view; b, girdle view. (1)
144. N. seriata. Part of a filament. (8)
145. N. linearis. Valve view. 92)
146. N. longissima. Cell outline. (8)
147. N. bilobata var. **minor.** a, valve view; b, girdle view. (8)

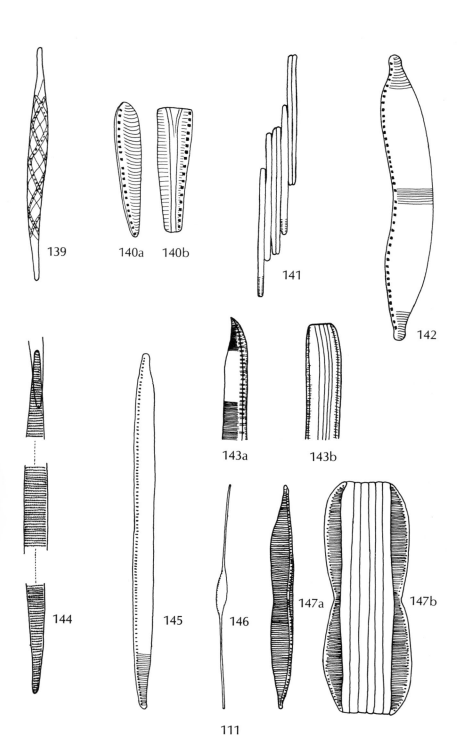

139

140a 140b

141

142

144 145 146 147a 147b

143a 143b

111

Figures 148-157

148. ***Neidium hitchcockii.*** Valve view. (22)
149. ***Anomoeoneis sphaerophora.*** Valve view. (2)
150. ***Caloneis amphisbaena.*** Valve view. (1)
151. ***Stauroneis phoenocentron.*** Valve view. (28)
152. ***Capartogramma crucicula.*** Valve view. (22)
153. ***Navicula mutica.*** Valve view. (28)
154. ***Oestrupia powelii.*** Valve view. (22)
155. ***Pinnularia gentilis.*** Valve view. (3)
156. ***Navicula membranacea.*** Part of a filament with one complete cell in girdle view. (8)
157. ***N. distans.*** a, valve view; b, girdle view. (8)

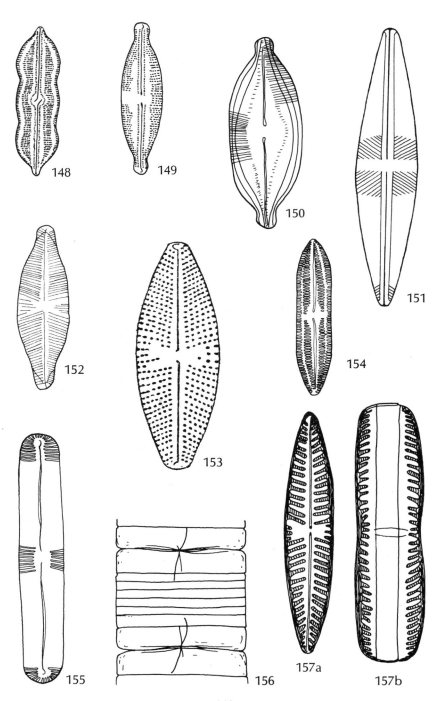

148

149

150

151

152

153

154

155

156

157a

157b

113

Figures 158-165

158. ***Frickia lewisiana.*** Valve view with raphe detail, the closely arranged striae omitted. (22)

159. ***Brebissonia boeckii.*** Valve view. (93)

160. ***Amphipleura pellucida.*** Valve view with striae omitted. (6)

161. ***Frustulia rhomboides.*** Valve view with striae omitted. (3)

162. ***Diatoma vulgare.*** a, valve view; b, zigzag chain with cells in view. (28)

163. ***Denticula pelagica*** var. ***intermedia.*** a, valve view below surface; b, girdle view. (2)

164. ***Diatomella balfouriana.*** a, valve view; b, girdle view. (22)

165. ***Tetracyclus lacustris.*** a, valve view with septa; b, girdle view. (2)

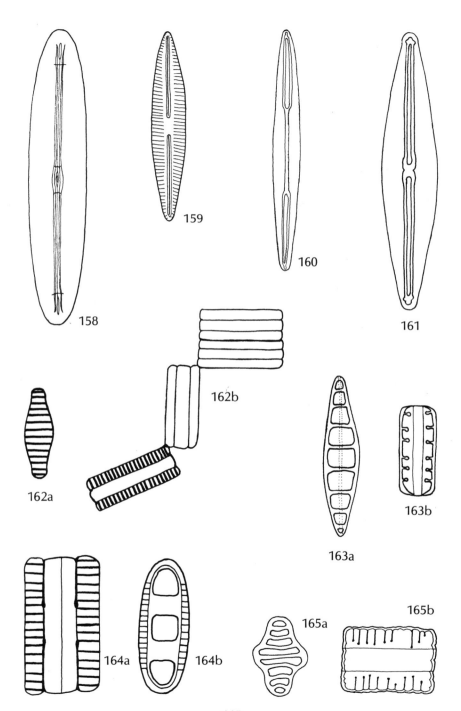

158

159

160

161

162b

162a

163a

163b

164a

164b

165a

165b

115

Figures 166-174

166. ***Tabellaria fenestrata.*** a, valve view with pseudoraphe; b, b, girdle view. (17)

167. ***Grammatophora angulosa.*** a, valve view with intercalary bands below surface; b, zigzag chain with cells in girdle view. (8)

168. ***G. marina*** Zigzag chain, the cells in girdle view. (8)

169. ***Tabellaria fenestrata.*** Zigzag chain with cells in girdle view. (17)

170. ***Fragilaria contruens.*** a, valve view; b, girdle view. (17)

171. ***Dimerogramma fulvum.*** a, valve view; b, girdle view. (26)

172. ***Grammatophora marina.*** a, valve view with intercalary bands below surface; b, girdle view. (8)

173. ***Mastogloia smithii*** var ***abnormis.*** a, valve view with surface striations; b, valve view below surface showing locules. (6)

174. ***Eunotia pectinalis.*** a, valve view; b, girdle view with capitate apices. (1)

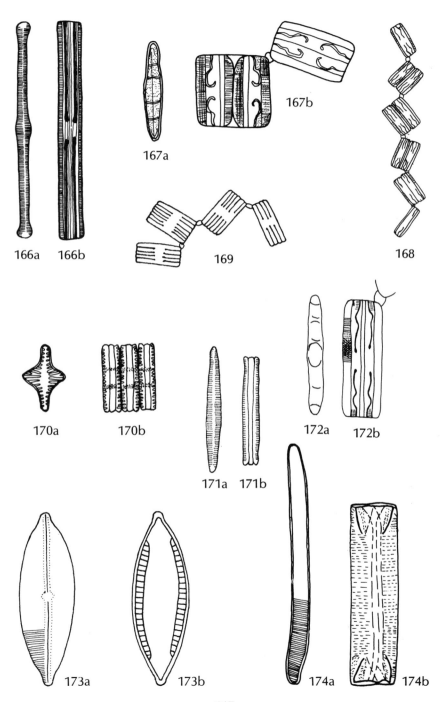

166a   166b

167a

167b

169

168

170a   170b   171a   171b   172a   172b

173a   173b   174a   174b

117

Figures 175-180

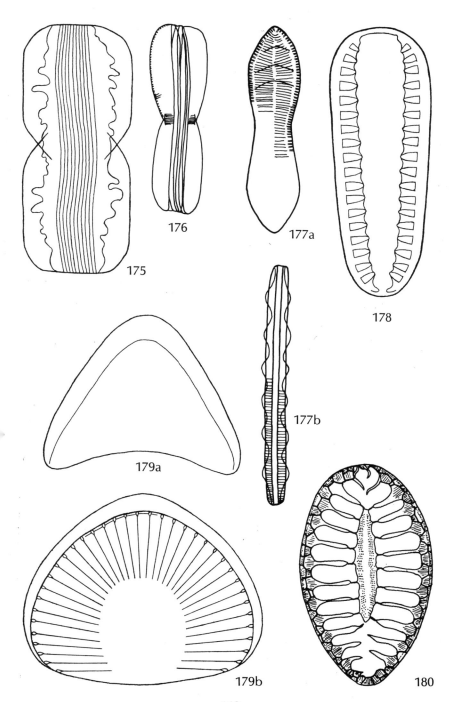

175

176

177a

178

177b

179a

179b

180

119